UP ONE
PAIR OF STAIRS

OF

MY BOOK HOUSE

EDITED BY

OLIVE BEAUPRÉ MILLER

PUBLISHERS

THE BOOK HOUSE for CHILDREN
CHICAGO

PREFACE

"UP ONE PAIR OF STAIRS" is the fitting title of this third
volume, since its object is to lead the child one step up out of
the nursery into a larger world. Thus this book gives him stories of child
life in other countries and introduces him to the more simple fairy tales,
for which he has not until now been ready, since, as I have mentioned in
my Foreword, the very young child, just learning the world of reality
about him, is confused by elves and fairies and does not know where to
place them in his thinking. But in this volume, as in all the others, care
has been taken to keep a good balance by offsetting imaginative tales
with tales of real life and by including humorous stories.

"Little Half-Chick" is a Spanish folk tale; "Oeyvind and Marit,"
written by the great Norwegian author, Björnstjerne Björnson, is a story
about two children in Norway. There is a Swedish tale, "The Cap That
Mother Made;" a Scotch folk tale, "The Wee, Wee Mannie and the Big,
Big Coo;" and a delightful German Christmas folk tale, "The Shoemaker
and the Elves." Goldilocks is here, a St. Valentine's Day story retold
from Chaucer, a tale from the fables of LaFontaine and more tales from
Aesop's Fables. At this period the child is most interested in animals, all
kinds of animals, and in stories about them, so this volume abounds in
such stories, including some verses telling for children of this age the
story of Kingsley's "Water Babies," with all the fascinating life of the sea.

As to poetry we have, among many other good things, "The Mock
Turtle's Song," from Lewis Carroll's classic for children, "Alice in
Wonderland;" "The Duck's Ditty" from Kenneth Grahame's famous
book, "The Wind in the Willows," and "King Hilary and the Beggarman," a delicious bit of nonsense from "Now We Are Six" by A. A.
Milne. Thus we have suggested for the attention of parents great children's
books, which they may wish to get and read as a whole to their children.

Also in "Up One Pair of Stairs" is the story of the babe, Moses, for all the earlier volumes and most of the later ones contain one Bible story.

This book was further designed to give children an acquaintance with the greatest English illustrators for children, whose work has delighted both children and adults for generations. In every child's library belong books illustrated by Kate Greenaway, Randolph Caldecott and Walter Crane. In Volume One there are two beautiful pages in full color from Kate Greenaway and here in Volume Three are two more pages by her. Famous for her charming little pictures of children and the quaint clothing she designed for them, Kate Greenaway also had the ability to write the lively, utterly childlike verses to go with her pictures, so the text and the drawings are one in spirit.

In addition to these illustrations by Kate Greenaway, Volume Three contains drawings by Randolph Caldecott with his inimitable sense of humor, his love of life and people. Caldecott's pictures are so full of funny little details that a child can look at them for a long time to find everything funny about them. Then maybe at last he will discover what he had not seen before—the nose and eyes of a man peeping very ridiculously over a high brick wall. Born, like Kate Greenaway, in 1846, Caldecott has been a favorite with children for almost four generations and no child should miss the fun of laughing at his pictures.

Walter Crane belonged to the late nineteenth century. With his love for pure decoration and design, he made his "A Baby's Own Aesop" the most beautiful edition of "Aesop's Fables" in existence. So Volume Three has two stories from Aesop with drawings after Walter Crane.

These three, Kate Greenaway, Randolph Caldecott and Walter Crane, are the most famous English illustrators for children out of the past. Thus these books introduce children to the best in art as well as in literature and music.

CONTENTS

THE WONDERFUL WORLD*
WILLIAM BRIGHTY RANDS

Great, wide, beautiful, wonderful World,
With the wonderful water round you curled,
And the wonderful grass upon your breast---
World, you are beautifully dressed.

*Reprinted by the courteous permission of John Lane Company.

The Cap That Mother Made

A SWEDISH TALE

Once upon a time there was a little boy, named Anders, and he had a new cap. A prettier cap was never seen, for his mother herself had knit it; and who could ever make anything half so nice as Mother! The cap was yellow, except a small part in the middle. That was blue, for there had not been enough yellow yarn to make it all; and the tassel was blue.

Anders' brothers and sisters walked about admiring him; then he put his hands in his pockets and went out for a walk, for he was altogether willing that everyone should see how fine his mother had made him.

The first person he met was a farmhand walking beside a cart loaded with peat, and bidding his horse gee-up. When he saw Anders' new cap, the farmhand made a bow so deep that he bent nearly double, but

Anders trotted proudly past him, holding his head very high.

At the turn of the road he came upon Lars, the tanner's boy. Lars was such a big boy that he wore high boots and carried a jack-knife. But oh, when he saw that cap, he stood quite still to gaze at it, and he could not help going up close to Anders and fingering the splendid blue tassel.

"I'll give you my cap for yours," he cried, "and my jack-knife besides!"

Now this knife was a splendid one, and Anders knew that as soon as one has a jack-knife, one is almost a man. But still he would not for all the world give up, for the knife, the cap which Mother had made.

"Oh, no, I could not do that," he said. And then he nodded good-bye to Lars, and went on his own way.

Soon after this Anders met a queer little lady. She curtsied to him until her skirts spread out about her like a balloon and she said: "Lad, you are so fine, why do you not go to the king's ball?"

"Yes, why do I not?" thought Anders. "With this cap, I am altogether fit to go and visit the king."

And off he went.

In the palace yard stood two soldiers with guns over their shoulders and shining helmets on their heads. When Anders went to pass them, they both leveled their guns at him.

"Where are you going?" asked one of the soldiers.

"I am going to the king's ball," answered Anders.

"No, you are not," said the other soldier, trying to push him back. "Nobody can go to the king's ball without a uniform."

But just at this moment the princess came tripping across the yard, dressed in a white satin gown, with ribbons of gold.

"This lad has no uniform, it's true," she said, "but he has a very fine cap and that will do just as well. He shall come to the ball."

So she took Anders by the hand and walked with him up the broad marble stairs, past the soldiers who

14

stood on every third step, through magnificent halls where gentlemen and ladies in silk and velvet were waiting about. And wherever Anders went, all the people bowed to him, for, as like as not, they thought him a prince when they saw what it was that he wore on his head.

At the farther end of the largest hall a table was set with long rows of golden plates and goblets. On huge silver platters were piles of tarts and cakes. The princess sat down under a blue canopy with bouquets of roses on it; and she bade Anders to sit in a golden chair by her side.

"But you must not eat with your cap on your head," she said, and she started to take it off.

"Oh, yes, I can eat just as well with it on," said Anders, and he held on to it with both his hands, for if it were taken away from him, he did not feel sure he would ever get it again.

"Well, well, give it to me," begged the princess, "and I will give you a kiss."

The princess was beautiful, and Anders would surely have liked to be kissed by her, but not for anything in this world would he give up the cap that Mother had made. He only shook his head.

Then the princess filled his pockets full of cakes; she put her own heavy gold chain around his neck, and bent down and kissed him.

"Now will you give me the cap?" she said.

Anders moved farther back in his chair, but he never once took his hands from his head.

Then the doors were thrown open and the king himself entered, accompanied by gentlemen in glittering uniforms and plumed hats. The king wore a mantle of blue velvet, bordered with ermine, and he had a large gold crown on his head.

When he saw Anders in the golden chair, he smiled.

"That is a very fine cap you have," he said.

"So it is," said Anders, "it is made of Mother's

best yarn, and she has knit it herself, and every one wants to get it away from me."

"But surely you would like to change caps with me," said the king, and he lifted his shining gold crown from his head.

Anders said never a word but when the king came nearer to him with his gold crown in one hand, and the other hand outstretched toward that beautiful cap, then, with one jump, Anders was out of his chair. Like an arrow he darted out of the hall, through the palace, down the stairs, and across the yard. He ran so fast that the necklace the princess had given him fell from his neck, and all the cakes rolled out of his pockets.

But he had his cap! He had his cap! He had his cap! With both hands he clutched it tight as he ran back home to his mother's cottage. "Well, Anders, where have you been?" cried his mother. So he told her all about what had happened.

All his brothers and sisters stood and listened with mouths wide open.

But when his big brother heard how he had

refused to give his cap in exchange for the king's golden crown, he cried out:

"Anders, you were foolish! Just think of all the things you might have bought with the king's gold crown! Velvet jackets and long leather boots and silken hose, and a sword. Besides, you could have bought yourself a much finer cap with a feather in it."

Anders' face grew red, very red. "I was not foolish," he answered. "I could never have bought a finer cap, not for all the king's crown. I could never have bought anything in all this world one half so fine as the cap my mother made me!"

Then his mother took him up on her lap, and kissed him.

THE ROAD TO CHINA
OLIVE BEAUPRÉ MILLER

I LEARNED today the world is round
  Like my big rubber ball,
With China on the other side,
  Down there below us all.

And so I went and dug a hole—
  I started in at eight—
And dug and dug and dug and dug,
  Beside the garden gate.

And oh, I thought, what fun 'twill be
  To get a ladder tall,
And climb right down to China through
  The hole behind the wall!

What fun to walk through little streets
  All lit with lanterns queer!
Each man will have a pig-tail, and
  How strange the talk I'll hear!

To think the road to China lies
  Just by our garden wall!
Then Daddy came and said, "Ho! Ho!
  That's not the way at all!

"To get to China, you must sail
  For days across the sea!"—
Why there's no short cut through the earth
  Seems very queer to me!

Goldilocks and the Three Bears*
AN ENGLISH FOLK TALE

ONCE upon a time there were three bears who lived in a little house of their own, in a wood. There was a great, huge bear who was the Father Bear; a middle-sized bear who was the Mother Bear; and a tiny, wee bear who was the Baby Bear. They had each a pot for their porridge—a little pot for the tiny, wee bear; a middle-sized pot for the middle-sized bear; and a great, huge pot for the great, huge bear. One morning the three bears found their porridge was too hot, so they left it to cool in their porridge pots and went out for a walk in the woods. While they were gone, a little girl came

*Long ago in "Scrapefoot," a tale from *Reynard the Fox*, the visitor to the Bears was a Fox. Robert Southey, the poet and friend of Coleridge, made an old woman the visitor, but the English people took the story over and substituted a pretty little girl.

along. She was called Goldilocks, because her hair shone like gold, and she, too, was out for a walk in the woods.

"I wonder who lives here," she said to herself, as she saw the funny little house. She knocked and she knocked and she knocked, but nobody came. Then, without ever stopping to think that she had no business to enter where she was not invited, she opened the door and peeped in. There on the table were the three pots of porridge—the great, huge pot; the middle-sized pot; and the tiny, wee pot. Goldilocks tasted the porridge in the great huge pot, but it was too hot. So she tasted the porridge in the middle-sized pot, but that was too cold. Then she tasted the porridge in the tiny, wee pot, and that was just right. So she ate it all up!

Now in the room she saw three chairs—a great, huge chair; a middle-sized chair; and a tiny, wee chair. So Goldilocks sat down in the great, huge chair, but that was too hard. Then she sat down in the middle-sized chair, but that was too soft. So she tried the tiny, wee chair, and that was just right! But, no sooner had she got quite comfortable than there was a crash and a bang! The tiny, wee chair broke into tiny, wee pieces and spilled Goldilocks on the floor.

So Goldilocks went into the bedroom. There she saw a great, huge bed; a middle-sized bed; and a tiny, wee bed. First, she lay down on the great, huge bed, but that was too hard. Then she lay down on the middle-sized bed, but that was too soft. At last she lay down on the tiny,

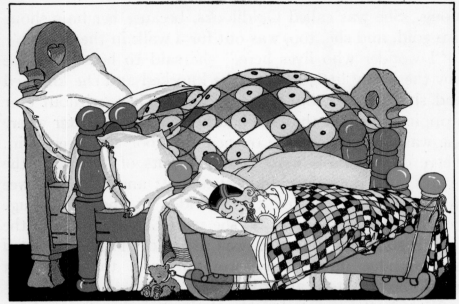

wee bed, and that was just right! So Goldilocks curled up under the covers and fell fast asleep.

After a while, along came the three bears who lived in the house—the great, huge bear who was the Father Bear; the middle-sized bear who was the Mother Bear; and the tiny, wee bear who was the Baby Bear.

When the great, huge bear saw his pot, he roared in his rough, gruff voice,

"WHO HAS BEEN TASTING MY PORRIDGE?"

When the middle-sized bear saw her pot, she cried out in her middle-sized voice,

"Who has been tasting my porridge?"

And when the tiny, wee bear saw his pot, he squealed in his tiny, wee voice,

"Who has been tasting my porridge and eaten it all up?"

When the great, huge bear saw his chair with the cushion all flattened down, he roared in his rough, gruff voice,

"WHO HAS BEEN SITTING IN MY CHAIR?"

And the middle-sized bear, when she saw the cushion all flattened down on her chair, cried in her middle-sized voice,

"Who has been sitting in my chair?"

And the tiny, wee bear, when he saw what had happened to his chair, squealed in his tiny, wee voice,

"Who has been sitting in my chair and broken it all to pieces?"

So they all went into the bedroom, and when the great, huge bear saw his bed with the covers all crumpled up, he roared in his rough, gruff voice,

"WHO HAS BEEN LYING ON MY BED?"

And the middle-sized bear, when she saw her bed with

the covers all crumpled up, cried in her middle-sized voice,

"Who has been lying on my bed?"

And the tiny, wee bear, when he looked at his bed, squealed in his tiny, wee voice,

"Here she is! Here she is! Fast asleep in my little bed!"

His voice woke Goldilocks and she opened her eyes.

"GR—R—!" growled the great, huge bear in his rough, gruff voice.

"Gr-r-r!" growled the middle-sized bear in her middle-sized voice.

"Gr-r-r!" growled the tiny, wee bear in his tiny, wee voice.

When Goldilocks heard them all growling around her, she was very sorry indeed that she hadn't stopped to think before she entered their house and meddled with their things. Before you could say, "Jack Robinson," she jumped out of bed, rushed to the window, climbed out, and ran back home as fast as her legs would carry her.

FAIRY AND CHILD
EUGENE FIELD

OH, listen, little Dear-My-Soul
    To the fairy voices calling,
For the moon is high
      in the misty sky
And the honey dew is falling;
To the midnight feast
      in the clover bloom
The bluebells are a-ringing,
And it's Come away
      to the land of fay,"
That the katydid is singing.

25

YES, that's the girl that struts about,
  She's very proud,—so very proud!
Her *bow-wow's* quite as proud as she;
They both are very wrong to be
  So proud—so very proud.

See, Jane and Willy laugh at her,
  They say she's very proud!
Says Jane, "My stars!—they're very silly;"
"Indeed they are," cries little Willy,
  "To walk so stiff and proud."

—*Kate Greenaway**

*Kate Greenaway is always associated with the illustrators, Caldecott and Crane, and also with John Ruskin, author of *Dame Wiggins of Lee*. They were friends for years, and she wrote Ruskin letters decorated with her dainty drawings.

S CHOOL is over,
    Oh, what fun!
Lessons finished,
    Play begun.
Who'll run fastest,
    You or I?
Who'll laugh loudest?
    Let us try.
            —*Kate Greenaway**

*Kate Greenaway is famous for her charming little pictures of children. As she began to draw the quaint costumes, inspired by her love of English country people, she dressed dolls as models in order to experiment with color and style.

THE OWL

ALFRED TENNYSON

When cats run home and light is come,
 And dew is cold upon the ground,
And the far-off stream is dumb,
 And the whirring sail goes round;
 And the whirring sail goes round;
  Alone and warming his five wits,
  The white owl in the belfry sits.

When merry milkmaids click the latch,
 And rarely smells the new-mown hay,
And the cock hath sung beneath the
  thatch
 Twice or thrice his roundelay;
 Twice or thrice his roundelay;
  Alone and warming his five wits,
  The white owl in the belfry sits.

28

The Owl's Answer to Tommy*

JULIANA HORATIA EWING

ONE evening Tommy's grandmother was telling him and his little brother Johnny about a Brownie who used to do all the work in a neighbor's house before the family got up in the morning.

"What was he like, Granny?" asked Tommy.

"Like a little man, they say, my dear."

"What did he do?"

"He came in before the family was up, and swept up the hearth, and lighted the fire, and set out the breakfast and tidied the room, and did all sorts of housework. He never would be seen and was off before they could catch him. But they could hear him laughing and playing about the house sometimes."

"Did they give him any wages, Granny?"

"No, my dear. He did it for love. They set a pancheon of clear water for him overnight, and now and then a bowl

*From *Brownies*, published by The Macmillan Company.
(*Brownie Scouts' official story*)

DOROTHY TODD

of bread and milk or cream. Sometimes he left a bit of money in the water. Sometimes he weeded the garden or threshed the corn. He saved endless trouble both to men and maids."

"Oh, Granny! Why did he go?"

"The maids caught sight of him one night, my dear, and his coat was so ragged, that they got a new suit and a linen shirt for him, and laid them by the bread and milk bowl. But when Brownie saw the things, he put them on and, dancing round the kitchen, sang,

" '*What have we here! Hemten hamten!*
Here will I nevermore tread nor stampen.'

UP ONE PAIR OF STAIRS

And away he danced through the door and never came back again."

"Oh, Grandmother! But why didn't he come back?"

"The Old Owl knows, my dear, I don't. Ask her."

Now Tommy was a lazy boy. He wished that he could find a brownie to tidy the room, and fetch the turf, and pick up chips, and do all his work for him. So that night, while little Johnny was off in the land of dreams, growing rosier and rosier as he slept, Tommy lay wide awake, thinking of his grandmother's story.

"There's an owl living in the old shed by the lake," he thought. "It may be *the* Old Owl herself, and she knows, Granny says. When father's gone to bed and the moon rises, I'll go and ask her."

By and by the moon rose like gold and went up into the heavens like silver, flooding the fields with a pale, ghostly light. Tommy crept softly down the ladder, through the kitchen and out on the moor. It was a glorious night, though everything but the wind and Tommy seemed asleep.

The stones, the walls, the gleaming lanes, were so intensely still, the church tower in the valley seemed awake and watching, but silent; the houses in the village round it had all their eyes shut; and it seemed to Tommy as if the very fields had drawn white sheets over them, and lay sleeping also.

"Hoot! hoot!" said a voice from the fir wood behind him. Somebody else was awake, then. "It's the Old Owl," said Tommy; and there she came swinging heavily across the moor with a flapping, stately flight, and sailed into the shed by the lake. The old lady moved faster than she appeared to do, and though Tommy ran hard she was in the shed some time before him. When he got in, no bird was to be seen, but he heard a sound from above, and there sat Old Owl, blinking at him—Tommy—with yellow eyes.

"Oh, dear!" said Tommy, for he didn't much like it.

"Come up, come up!" said she hoarsely.

She could speak then! Beyond all doubt it was *the* Old Owl, and none other.

"Come up here! Come up here!" said the Old Owl.

Tommy had often climbed up for fun to the beam that ran across the shed where the Old Owl sat. He climbed up now, and sat face to face with her, and thought her eyes looked as if they were made of flame.

"Now, what do you want?" said the Owl.

"Please," said Tommy, "can you tell me where to find the brownies, and how to get one to come and live with us?"

"Oohoo!" said the Owl, "that's it, is it? I know of two brownies."

"Hurrah!" said Tommy. "Where do they live?"

"In your house," said the Owl.

Tommy was aghast.

"In our house!" he exclaimed. "Whereabouts? Let me rummage them out. Why do they do nothing?"

"One of them is too young," said the Owl.

"But why doesn't the other work?" asked Tommy.

"He is idle, he is idle," said the Old Owl, and she gave herself such a shake as she said it that the fluff went flying through the shed, and Tommy nearly tumbled off the beam.

"Then we don't want him," said he. "What is the use of

having brownies if they do nothing to help us? But perhaps if you would tell me where to find them," said Tommy, "I could tell them what to do."

"Could you?" said the Owl. "Oohoo! Oohoo!" Tommy couldn't tell whether she were hooting or laughing.

"Of course I could," he said. "They might be up and sweep the house, and light the fire, and spread the table, and that sort of thing, before Father came down. The Brownie did all that in Granny's mother's young days. And they might tidy the room, and fetch the turf, and pick up my chips, and sort Granny's scraps. Oh! there's plenty to do."

"So there is," said the Owl. "Oohoo! Well, I can tell you where to find one of the brownies: and, if you can find him, he will tell you where his brother is. But all this depends upon whether you will follow my directions."

"I am quite ready to go," said Tommy, "and I will do as you tell me. I feel sure I could persuade them to come; if they only knew how every one would love them if they made themselves useful!"

"Oohoo! Oohoo!" said the Owl. "Now pay attention. You must go to the north side of the lake when the moon is shining—('I know brownies like water,'muttered Tommy) —and turn yourself round three times, saying this charm:

'Twist me and turn me and show me the Elf—
I looked in the water and saw—'

When you have got so far look into the water, and think

34

of a word that will rhyme with Elf, and at the same moment you will see the brownie."

"Is the brownie a merman," said Tommy, "that he lives under water?"

"That depends on whether he has a fish's tail," said the Owl, "and that you can see for yourself."

"Well, the moon is shining, so I shall go," said Tommy. "Good-by, and thank you, Ma'am." And he jumped down and went, saying to himself, "I believe he is a merman, all the same, or else how could he live in the lake?"

The moon shone very brightly on the center of the lake. Tommy knew the place well, for there was a fine echo there. Round the edges grew rushes and water plants, and, turning himself three times, as the Old Owl had told him, he repeated the charm:

35

"Twist me and turn me and show me the Elf—
I looked in the water and saw—"

Now for it! He looked in—and saw his own face.

"Why, there's no one there but myself!" said Tommy. "And what can the word be? I must have done it wrong."

"Wrong!" said the Echo.

Tommy was almost surprised to find the echo awake at this time of night.

"Much you know whether I'm wrong or not," said he. "Belf! Celf! Delf! Felf! Helf! Jelf! There can't be a word to fit the rhyme. And then to look for a brownie and see nothing but myself!"

"Myself," said the Echo.

"Will you be quiet?" said Tommy. "If you would tell me the word, there would be some sense in your interference; but to roar 'Myself!' at me, which neither rhymes nor runs—it does rhyme, though, as it happens," he added, "how very odd, it runs, too!

'Twist me and turn me and show me the Elf—
I looked in the water and saw myself!'

Which I certainly did. What can it mean? The Old Owl knows, as Granny would say; so I shall go back and ask her."

And back he went. There sat the Old Owl as before.

"Oohoo!" said she, as Tommy climbed up. "What did you see in the lake?"

36

"I saw nothing but myself," said Tommy, indignantly.

"And what did you expect to see?" asked the Owl.

"I expected to see a brownie," said Tommy, "you told me so."

"And what are brownies like, pray?" inquired the Owl.

"The one Granny knew was a useful little fellow, something like a little man," said Tommy.

"Ah!" said the Owl, "but you know at present this one is an idle fellow, something like a little man. Oohoo! Oohoo! Are you quite sure you didn't see him?"

"Quite," answered Tommy sharply, "I saw no one but myself."

"Hoot! Toot! How touchy we are! And who are you, pray?"

"I'm not a brownie," said Tommy.

"Don't be too sure," said the Owl. "Did you find out the word that rhymed with Elf?"

"No." said Tommy, "I could find no word with any meaning that would rhyme, except, 'myself.' "

"Well, if 'myself' rhymes," said the Owl, "what more do you want?"

"I don't understand," said Tommy humbly, "you know I'm not a brownie."

"Yes, you are," said the Owl, "and a very idle one, too. All children are brownies."

"But I couldn't do work like a brownie," said Tommy.

"Why not?" inquired the Owl. "Couldn't you sweep the floor, light the fire, spread the table, tidy the room, fetch the turf, pick up your own chips and sort your grand-mother's scraps?''

"Please," said Tommy, "I should like to go home now and tell Johnny."

"Very well," said the Owl, "I think I had better take you."

"I know the way, thank you," said Tommy.

"Do as I say," said the Owl. "Lean your full weight against me and shut your eyes."

Tommy laid his head against the Owl's feathers. Down he sank and sank. He could feel nothing solid. He jumped with a start to save himself, opened his eyes, and found that he was sitting in the loft with Johnny sleeping by his side. And what was odder still, it was no longer moonlight, but early dawn. "Get up, Johnny, I've a story to tell you," he cried. And while Johnny sat up and rubbed his eyes, he told him all about it.

And after that Tommy and Johnny were the most useful little brownies in that whole country.

THE ELF AND THE
DORMOUSE

OLIVER HERFORD

UNDER a toadstool crept a wee Elf,
　Out of the rain, to shelter himself.

Under the toadstool sound asleep,
Sat a big Dormouse all in a heap.

Trembled the wee Elf, frightened, and yet
Fearing to fly away lest he get wet.

To the next shelter—maybe a mile!
Sudden the wee Elf smiled a wee smile.

Tugged till the toadstool toppled in two.
Holding it over him, gayly he flew.

Soon he was safe home, dry as could be.
Soon woke the Dormouse—"Good gracious me!"

"Where is my toadstool?" loud he lamented,
And that's how umbrellas first were invented.

39

THE BROWNIES IN THE TOY SHOP*

PALMER COX

AS shades of evening settled down,
The Brownies rambled through the town,
To pry at this, to pause at that,
By something else to hold a chat.

At length before a store, their eyes
Were fixed with wonder and surprise
On toys of wood, and wax, and tin,
And toys of rubber piled within.
Said one, "In all our wandering 'round,
A sight like this we never found."

*Palmer Cox's busy little brownies first appeared in the pages of *St. Nicholas* in the 1890's and were so loved by children that the chief characters were reproduced as dolls. By permission of The Century Co.

Another said, "It must be here
Old Santa Claus comes every year
To gather up his large supply,
When Christmas Eve is drawing nigh."

Not long were they content to view
Through window panes those wonders new;
And, in a manner quite their own,
They made their way through wood and stone.

And then surprises met the band,
In odd conceits from every land.
Well might the Brownies stand and stare
At all the objects crowded there!

There horses stood for boys to ride;
Here boats were waiting for the tide.
There soldiers stood in warlike bands;
And naked dolls held out their hands.
This way and that, the Brownies ran;
To try the toys they soon began.

The Jack-in-box, so quick and strong,
With staring eyes and whiskers long,
Now o'er and o'er was set and sprung
Until the wig was from it flung;
And then they crammed him in his case,
With wig and night-cap in their place.

The trumpets, drums,
     and weapons bright*
Soon filled them all with great delight.
Like troops preparing for their foes,
In single ranks and double rows,
With swords of tin and guns of wood,
They wheeled about,
     and marched or stood.
They went through skirmish drill and all,
From room to room by bugle-call;

*In *The Toy Symphony*, Joseph Haydn (1732–1809), the teacher of Mozart and Beethoven, wrote a part for the toys and bird calls he loved as a boy. You can hear the drum, the bells, the cuckoo, the bob-white, and the nightingale.

The music-box poured forth an air
That charmed the dullest spirits there,
Till, yielding to the pleasing sound,
They danced with dolls a lively round.*

There fish were working tail and fin
In seas confined by wood and tin;
The canvas shark and rubber whale
Seemed ill content in dish or pail,
And leaping all obstructions o'er
Performed their antics on the floor.

Some found at marbles greatest fun,
And still they played, and still they won.

More gave the singing tops no rest—
But kept them spinning at their best.

*The Waltzing Doll (Poupée Valsante) by the Viennese pianist, Edward Poldini, is a charming little imitation of a dancing doll.

The rocking-horse that wildly rose,
Now on its heels, now on its nose,
Was forced to bear so great a load,
It seemed to founder on the road,
Then tumble feebly to the floor,
Never to lift a rocker more.

Thus, through the shop in greatest glee,
They rattled 'round, the sights to see,
Till stars began to dwindle down,
And morning crept into the town.
And then, with all the speed they knew,
Away to forest shades they flew.

NEW YEAR'S DAY
Olive Beaupré Miller

ON New Year's Day the children laugh
    And never, never cry,
Glad bells ring out their ding-dong-ding,
    This is the reason why—

The people sat around last night,
    The clock went tick, tick, tock,
And lo, a tiny stranger came
    To earth at twelve o'clock.

Grandpa Old Year ran away,
    He ran away in flight;
Little Baby New Year 'twas,
    Who came to earth last night!

THE CIRCUS PARADE*
OLIVE BEAUPRÉ MILLER

O GOODY, it's coming, the circus parade
    And all the way up the street,
What crowds of people in gay-colored clothes,
    With popcorn and peanuts to eat!

The children have red, blue, and yellow balloons,
    As up by the curbing they stand,
And now, in the distance, we suddenly hear
    The circus's big brass band!

*The marches of the American March King, John Philip Sousa, especially *The Stars and Stripes Forever*, have been played by the brilliantly-dressed circus band for many a circus parade.

46

Behind the crash-bang! of the music they play,
   Come riders in red velvet gowns,
And after them doing the funniest things,
   A silly procession of clowns.

Then lions and tigers that pace up and down,
   In wagons all painted with gold,
And monkeys a-playing just all kinds of tricks,
   As they grimace and chatter and scold.

O, next there come camels and elephants, too,
   High on their backs men ride;
There are queer little ponies, no bigger than dogs,
   With a clown on a donkey, beside!

And then there come chariots rumbling by
   With horses all four in a row;
And the wheezing, old, piping calliope is
   The very tail end of the show!

CLOUDS

WHITE sheep, white sheep,
On a blue hill,
When the wind stops,
You all stand still;
When the wind blows,
You walk away slow.
White sheep, white sheep,
Where do you go?

Peter Rabbit Decides to Change His Name

THORNTON W. BURGESS

PETER RABBIT! Peter Rabbit! I don't see what Mother Nature ever gave me such a common-sounding name as that for. People laugh at me, but if I had a fine-sounding name they wouldn't laugh. Some folks say that a name doesn't amount to anything, but it does. If I should do some wonderful thing, nobody would think anything of it. No, sir, nobody would think anything of it at all just because—why just because it was done by Peter Rabbit."

Peter was talking out loud, but he was talking to himself. He sat in the dear Old Briar-patch with an ugly scowl on his usually happy face. The sun was shining;

From *The Adventures of Peter Cottontail.* Used by special arrangement with the author and publishers, Little, Brown & Company.

the Merry Little Breezes of Old Mother West Wind were dancing over the Green Meadows; the birds were singing; and happiness, the glad, joyous happiness of springtime, was everywhere but in Peter Rabbit's heart. There, there seemed to be no room for anything but discontent. And such foolish discontent—discontent with his name! And yet, do you know, there are lots of little people just as foolish as Peter Rabbit.

"Well, what are you going to do about it?"

The voice made Peter jump and turn around hastily. There was Jimmy Skunk poking his head in at the opening of one of Peter's private little paths. He was grinning, and Peter knew by that grin that Jimmy had heard what he had said. Peter didn't know what to say. He hung his head in a very shame-faced way.

"You've got something to learn," said Jimmy Skunk.

"What is it?" asked Peter.

"It's just this," replied Jimmy.

"There's nothing in a name except

> Just what we choose to make it.
> It lies with us and no one else
> How other folks shall take it.
> It's what we do and what we say
> And how we live each passing day
> That makes it big or makes it small
> Or even worse than none at all.
> A name just stands for what we are;
> It's what we choose to make it.
> And that's the way and only way
> That other folks will take it."

Peter Rabbit made a face at Jimmy Skunk. "I don't like being preached to."

"I'm not preaching; I'm just telling you what you ought to know without being told," replied Jimmy Skunk. "If you don't like your name, why don't you change it?"

"What's that?" cried Peter sharply.

"If you don't like your name, why don't you change it?" repeated Jimmy.

Peter sat up and the disagreeable frown had left his face. "I—I—hadn't thought of that," he said slowly. "Do you suppose I could, Jimmy Skunk?"

"Easiest thing in the world," replied Jimmy Skunk. "Just decide what name you like and then ask all your friends to call you by it."

"I believe I will!" cried Peter Rabbit.

"Well, let me know what it is when you have decided," said Jimmy, as he started for home. And all the way up the Crooked Little Path, Jimmy chuckled to himself as he thought of Foolish Peter Rabbit trying to change his name.

Peter Rabbit had quite lost his appetite. When Peter forgets to eat you may make up your mind that Peter has something very important to think about. At least he has something on his mind that he thinks is important. The fact is, Peter had fully made up his mind to change his name. He thought Peter Rabbit too common a name. But, when he tried to think of a better one, he found that no name that he could think of really pleased him anymore. So he thought, and he thought, and he thought, and he thought.

Now Jimmy Skunk was the only one to whom Peter had told how discontented he was with his name, and it was Jimmy who had suggested to Peter that he change it. Jimmy thought it a great joke, and he straightway passed the word along among all the little meadow and forest people that Peter Rabbit was going to change his name.

Everybody laughed and chuckled over the thought of Peter Rabbit's foolishness, and they planned to have a great deal of fun with Peter as soon as he should tell them his new name.

Peter was sitting on the edge of the Old Briar-patch one morning when Ol' Mistah Buzzard passed, flying low.

"Good mo'ning, Brer Cottontail," said Ol' Mistah Buzzard, with a twinkle in his eye.

At first Peter didn't understand that Ol' Mistah Buzzard was speaking to him, and, by the time he did, it was too late to reply for Ol' Mistah Buzzard was way, way up in the blue, blue sky.

"Cottontail, Cottontail," said Peter over and over to himself and began to smile. Every time he said it, he liked it better. "Cottontail, Peter Cottontail! How much better sounding that is than Peter Rabbit! That sounds as if I really was somebody. Yes, Sir, that's the very name I want. Now I must send word to all my friends that hereafter I am no longer Peter Rabbit, but Peter Cottontail."

Peter kicked up his heels in just the funny way he always does when he is pleased.

Suddenly he remembered that such a fine, long,

high-sounding name as Peter Cottontail demanded dignity. So he stopped kicking up his heels and began to practice putting on airs. But first he called to the Merry Little Breezes and told them about his change of name and asked them to tell all his friends that, in the future, he would not answer to the name of Peter Rabbit, but only to the name of Peter Cottontail. He was very grave, and earnest, and important, as he explained it to the Merry Little Breezes. The Merry Little Breezes kept their faces straight while he was talking, but as soon as they had left him to carry his message, they burst out laughing. It was such a joke!

And they giggled as they delivered his message to each of the little forest and meadow people:

"Peter Rabbit's changed his name.
In future without fail
You must call him, if you please,
Mr. Peter Cottontail."

While they were doing this, Peter was back in the Old Briar-patch practicing new airs and trying to look very high and mighty and important, as became one with such a fine-sounding name as Peter Cottontail.

Bobby Coon and Jimmy Skunk had their heads together. Now when these two put their heads together, you may make up your mind that they are planning mischief. Yes, sir, there is sure to be

mischief afoot when Bobby Coon and Jimmy Skunk put their heads together as they were doing now. Had Peter Rabbit seen them, he might not have felt so easy in his mind as he did. But Peter didn't see them. He was too much taken up with trying to look as important as his new name sounded. He was putting on airs and holding his head very high as he went down to the Smiling Pool to call on Jerry Muskrat. Whenever anyone called him by his first name, Peter pretended not to hear. He pretended that he had never heard that name and didn't know that he was being spoken to.

Bobby Coon and Jimmy Skunk thought it a great joke and they made up their minds that they would have some fun with Peter and, perhaps, make him see how foolish he was. Yes, sir, they planned to teach Peter a lesson. Bobby Coon hurried away to find Reddy Fox and tell him that Peter had gone down to the Smiling Pool and that, if he hid beside the path, he might catch Peter on the way back. Jimmy Skunk hunted up Blacky the Crow and Sammy Jay and told them of his plan and what he wanted them to do. Of course they promised that they would. Then he went to Ol' Mistah Buzzard and told him. Ol' Mistah Buzzard grinned and promised that he would do his share. Then Bobby Coon and Jimmy Skunk hid where they could see all that would happen.

Peter reached the Smiling Pool and now sat on the bank admiring his own reflection in the water and talking to Jerry Muskrat. He had just told Jerry that when his old name was called out he didn't hear it anymore, when along came Blacky the Crow.

"Hello, Peter Rabbit! You're just the fellow I am looking for; I've a very important message for you," shouted Blacky.

Peter kept right on talking with Jerry Muskrat, just as if he didn't hear, although he was burning with curiosity to know what the message was.

"I say, Peter Rabbit, are you deaf?" shouted Blacky the Crow. Jerry

56

Marguerite Davis.

Muskrat looked up at Blacky and winked. "Peter Rabbit isn't here," said he. "This is Peter Cottontail."

"Oh!" said Blacky. "My message is for Peter Rabbit, and it's something he really ought to know. I'm sorry he isn't here." And with that, away flew Blacky the Crow, chuckling to himself.

Peter looked quite as uncomfortable as he felt, but of course he couldn't say a word after boasting that he didn't hear people who called him Peter Rabbit. Pretty soon along came Sammy Jay. Sammy seemed very much excited.

"Oh, Peter Rabbit, I'm so glad I've found you!" he cried. "I've some very important news for you!"

Peter had all he could do to sit still and pretend not to hear, but he did.

"This is Peter Cottontail," said Jerry Muskrat, winking at Sammy Jay.

"Oh," replied Sammy, "my news is for Peter Rabbit," and off he flew, chuckling to himself.

Peter looked and felt more uncomfortable than ever. He bade Jerry Muskrat good-day and started for the dear Old Briar-patch to think things over. When he was half-way there, Ol' Mistah Buzzard came sailing down out of the sky.

"Brer Cottontail," said he, "if yo' see anything of Brer Rabbit, yo' tell him that Brer Fox am hiding behind the big bunch of grass just ahead."

Peter stopped short, and his heart gave a great leap. There, behind the clump of grass, was something red, sure enough. Peter didn't wait to see more. He started for a hiding-place he knew of in the Green Forest as fast as he could go, and behind him raced Reddy Fox. As he ran, he heard Blacky the Crow and Sammy Jay laughing; and then he knew that this was the news that they had had for him.

"I—I—guess that Peter Rabbit is a good enough name, after all," he panted.

UP ONE PAIR OF STAIRS

The Battle of the Firefly and the Apes

A FILIPINO TALE

WHEN the sun goes down in the Philippine Islands, darkness comes quickly and the myriad little lamps of the fireflies begin to glimmer among the trees. One evening, a firefly went to visit a friend. As he flew quietly along, carrying his little lamp and minding his own affairs, he met an ape. Said the ape, "Ho, ho, Mr. Firefly, why do you always carry a light?"

"I carry a light so that I can see the mosquitoes and keep out of their way," answered the firefly.

"Keep out of the way of the mosquitoes!" cried the ape. "You coward! You're afraid of the mosquitoes!"

"I'm not a coward! I'm not afraid of the mosquitoes!" said the firefly. "I go my way and mind my own affairs, and I leave the mosquitoes alone to go their way."

But the ape insisted that the firefly was afraid; and, the next day, he told all his ape friends that the firefly carried a lamp because he was a coward. So all the apes laughed and made sport of the firefly.

Now the firefly soon heard what Mr. Ape had said and how all the apes were laughing at him, so he resolved to teach them a lesson. He hurried off at once to Mr. Ape's house. Mr. Ape was asleep, but the firefly flashed his lamp in his face and woke him with a start.

"Why did you tell everyone that I was a coward?" he demanded. "Tomorrow come to the plaza and there, in

59

the sight of everyone, we will prove whether I am a coward!"

"Ho, ho, ho!" laughed the ape, "so you're offering to fight with *me*? Well, who are you going to bring to help you? One of your size will scarcely stand up alone against such a powerful creature as I am!"

"I shall come alone," said the firefly.

"Come alone! That's good!" cried the ape. "I shall bring a whole company of apes! I shall have a thousand at least—each one as big as myself! Then we shall see what will happen to you if you dare to come alone!"

So Mr. Ape ordered each of his friends to get a great club and meet him on the plaza. They all came in a crowd, but they found the one small firefly waiting there alone. Mr. Ape drew his company up in line and put himself at their head, then he fiercely gave the order to go forward against the firefly. But the firefly swiftly flew over and lit on the great ape's nose. The ape, who stood next in line, struck savagely at the firefly but the firefly darted nimbly out of reach, so the club missed him altogether and fell square on the great ape's nose! Flat fell Mr. Ape to the ground!

Then the firefly hurried to the second ape's nose. The third ape struck at his foe, but the firefly dodged out of the way just as he had before and the blow fell square on the second ape's nose! He, too, fell flat to the earth!

So it went on all down the line of apes. Each ape aimed his club at the firefly on his neighbor's nose, each ape missed the firefly and knocked his neighbor flat. Over they

bowled, one after another, just like a row of ninepins.

At last the firefly was left victorious over every one of his fallen foes! "Who now can say that the firefly is afraid?" he cried.

The apes cowered, shamefaced, on the ground with never a word to say. But the firefly flew quietly away, to mind his own affairs as before.

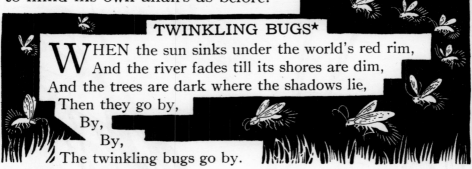

TWINKLING BUGS*

WHEN the sun sinks under the world's red rim,
    And the river fades till its shores are dim,
And the trees are dark where the shadows lie,
    Then they go by,
        By,
            By,
    The twinkling bugs go by.

*In *Little Firefly*, Charles Wakefield Cadman, American composer of music inspired by Indian themes, paints a dainty picture of the firefly as it flits here and there, flashing its little light through the dark night on the prairie.

DUCKS' DITTY*

KENNETH GRAHAME

ALL along the backwater,
  Through the rushes tall,
Ducks are a-dabbling,
Up tails all!

Ducks' tails, drakes' tails,
Yellow feet a-quiver,
Yellow bills all out of sight,
Busy in the river!

Slushy green undergrowth
Where the roach swim—
Here we keep our larder,
Cool and full and dim.

Every one for what he likes!
We like to be
Heads down, tails up,
Dabbling free!

*From "*The Wind in the Willows*," one of the great classics for children. Used by permission of the publishers, Charles Scribner's Sons. Kenneth Grahame, born in Scotland in 1859, also wrote "*The Golden Age*" and "*Dream Days*," two other great books for children.

The Mad Dog

Based on the poem by Oliver Goldsmith and on the illustrations for that poem done by Randolph Caldecott*

ONCE there was a man who had a dog, a nice little dog. The dog loved the man and the man loved the dog. Sometimes when he was at table, the man gave Little Dog a piece of meat before he himself had even started to eat. And Little Dog wagged his tail and looked up lovingly at his master. So all went well with the man and Little Dog.

Then the man got a cat, a little black cat and he loved the cat, too. He would play with the cat and stroke her nice soft fur. Well, that made Little Dog angry. He wanted his master to pet just him, just him, nobody but him! So whenever his master petted the cat, Little Dog crept off and sulked in a corner with one ear up and the other ear down.

One day the master left the room after petting his cat and the cat ran out of doors. Little Dog was in a huff! He was green-eyed with envy. He sprang up on his hind legs! He leapt about like mad! His hair stood up on end. He growled, he snarled, he yapped, he rolled his eyes, he showed his teeth! He wanted to chew that cat up, so he tore after her out the door.

*Born in 1846, the same year as Kate Greenaway, Randolph Caldecott was one of the masters of English illustration.

Away he went up the street, itching to get that cat! And he was in such a rage, he was so boiling with anger that he fairly frothed at the mouth. His tongue hung out and he looked mean, he did. He looked as mean as he felt.

A pretty young lady saw him. She was at the pump, pumping water into a bucket and she lifted up her eyebrows and opened her mouth in surprise.

"What on earth is the matter with that dog?" she wondered.

Then an old man leaned over the wall. He looked through his spectacles at Little Dog, and he cried:

"That dog! He must be mad! Run, run! He may bite you!"

At that the young lady shrieked. She left her bucket where it was by the pump and she ran off in a fright, shouting:

"Beware that dog! He's mad!"

So all the people who heard her and saw Little Dog come plunging wildly toward them started to run and shout in terror:

"Beware that dog! He's mad!"

One man climbed a tree. He shot up that tree so fast he lost his hat, he
lost his wig, he left his shiny bald head uncovered. Another man scrambled
over a wall with his coat-tails flying. A terrified woman tried to hide herself behind her umbrella and a mother dragged her little girl in a hurry into
the house. And all because of Little Dog!

Soon everybody was crying:

"Beware that dog! He's mad! Run, run! He may bite you!"

And everybody started running. Little girls ran, women ran! They were all a-flutter, a-twitter! Boys ran, men ran! Fat men ran, huffing, puffing! Thin men ran, their eyes opened wide in fright! And people looked out of windows to see what the hubbub was all about. Such a hurry, such a flurry, such an uproar, such a tumult! Then other dogs joined in the chase, yipping, yapping, jumping at people's heels and finding the chase great fun. But now with so many dogs tearing wildly about, nobody knew which one was the mad dog. So they raced now this way, now that, fleeing now from this dog and now from that one. And the more they raced the more the dogs chased and the wilder the tumult grew.

By-and-by the cat ran up a tree. Then Little Dog and the other dogs stopped chasing along with the people. They gathered around that tree, leaping and barking up at the cat. At that a man shouted, "We're safe! Those dogs were only chasing a cat!" And he ran up the street poking his head in at opened windows to tell everyone the danger was over.

So the town grew quiet again. Some people walked off in a very stately way, trying to pretend they'd never run from a dog, but a jolly fat man and two friends went off, arm in arm, laughing over the joke. And the jolly fat man cried: "To think we ran away from that dog who was only chasing a cat!"

But after a time the dogs got tired of waiting for the cat to come down and they also went home. Even Little Dog went home, thinking the cat would stay up the tree for good. He ran back to his master leaping for joy and his master took him on his knee and petted and stroked him. Then, behold, the little black cat came home, too. And when he saw the cat Little Dog went mad again. He growled and snarled and showed his teeth to keep her from coming to his master. And the cat humped up her back and spit and showed her claws.

Then the master picked the cat up and put her on his other knee and stroked her also.

"See here, you two," he said. "I love you both. And I'll love neither one of you half so well if you want me to love you only. You've got to stop fighting each other and learn to play together."

Then Little Dog yipp-yipped twice more at the cat and the cat spit twice more at the dog. But the master kept on stroking them, so at last they quieted down and yipped and spit no more.

The next day when Little Dog went out the gate before his master's house and into the street, all the other dogs came running and barking to ask him to chase the cat again. But that morning, for the very first time, Little Dog had played with the cat. She was a lively little cat and they had had fun together. So Little Dog barked to the other dogs:

"Bow-wow! Why chase a cat? Let's chase each other!"

KING HILARY AND THE
BEGGARMAN*

A. A. MILNE

Good King Hilary
Said to his Chancellor
(Proud Lord Willoughby,
Lord High Chancellor):
"Run to the wicket-gate
Quickly, quickly,
Run to the wicket-gate
        And see who is knocking.
It may be a rich man,
Sea-borne from Araby,
Bringing me peacocks,
Emeralds and ivory;
It may be a poor man,
Travel-worn and weary,
Bringing me oranges
        To put in my stocking."

*Taken from "Now We Are Six" by A. A. Milne, published and copyrighted, 1927, by E. P. Dutton & Co., Inc., New York. "Winnie-the-Pooh," "The Christopher Robin Story Book" and other books which Milne wrote for his own son, Christopher Robin, belong among the classics for children. The illustrations for this poem, with the exception of those on pages 70 and 74, were drawn by Ernest H. Shepard, whose decorations for Milne's books are almost as famous as the stories and poems themselves.

Proud Lord Willoughby,
Lord High Chancellor,
    Laughed both loud and free:*
"I've served Your Majesty, man to man,
Since first Your Majesty's reign began,
And I've often walked, but I never, never ran,
    Never, never, never," quoth he.

Good King Hilary
Said to his Chancellor
(Proud Lord Willoughby,
Lord High Chancellor):
"Walk to the wicket-gate
Quickly, quickly,
Walk to the wicket-gate
    And see who is knocking.

       *Haw! Haw! Haw!

It may be a captain,
Hawk-nosed, bearded,
Bringing me gold-dust,
Spices, and sandalwood:

It may be a scullion,
Care-free, whistling,
Bringing me sugar-plums
    To put in my stocking."

Proud Lord Willoughby,
Lord High Chancellor,
    Laughed both loud and free:
"I've served in the Palace since I was four,
And I'll serve in the Palace a-many years more,
And I've opened a window, but never a door,
    Never, never, never," quoth he.

Good King Hilary
Said to his Chancellor
(Proud Lord Willoughby,
Lord High Chancellor):
"Open the window
Quickly, quickly,
Open the window
    And see who is knocking.

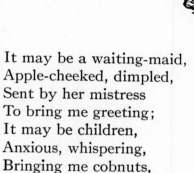

It may be a waiting-maid,
Apple-cheeked, dimpled,
Sent by her mistress
To bring me greeting;
It may be children,
Anxious, whispering,
Bringing me cobnuts,
    To put in my stocking."

Proud Lord Willoughby,
Lord High Chancellor,
    Laughed both loud and free:
"I'll serve Your Majesty till I die—
As Lord Chancellor, not as spy
To peep from lattices; no, not I,
    Never, never, never," quoth he.

Good King Hilary
Looked at his Chancellor
(Proud Lord Willoughby,
Lord High Chancellor):
He said no word
To his stiff-set Chancellor,
But ran to the wicket-gate
    To see who was knocking.

He found no rich man
Trading from Araby;
He found no captain,
Blue-eyed, weather-tanned;
He found no waiting-maid
Sent by her mistress;
But only a beggarman
    With one red stocking.

Good King Hilary
Looked at the beggarman,
    And laughed him three times three;
And he turned that beggarman round about:
"Your thews are strong, and your arm is stout;
Come, throw me a Lord High Chancellor out,
    And take his place," quoth he.

Of Hilary the Good and Great
Old wives at Christmas time relate
This tale, which points, at any rate,
    Two morals on the way.
The first: "*Whatever Fortune brings,*
Don't be afraid of doing things."
(Especially, of course, for Kings.)
    It also seems to say
(But not so wisely): "*He who begs*
With one red stocking on his legs
Will be, as sure as eggs are eggs,
    A Chancellor some day."

The Foolish, Timid, Little Hare

AN EAST INDIAN FABLE

ONCE there was a foolish, timid, little Hare, who was always expecting something awful to happen. She was forever saying, "Suppose the earth were to crack and swallow me up!" She said this over and over again till at last she really believed the earth was about to crack and swallow her up.

One day she was asleep under a palm tree when some Monkeys above dropped a cocoanut down. The little Hare didn't see the cocoanut, but she heard its thud on the ground. Up she jumped in a hurry and cried: "Dear me! The earth is surely cracking!" And she ran away as fast as she could, without ever looking behind her.

Presently she met an older Hare, who called out after her, "Why are you running so fast?"

The foolish, timid, little Hare answered, "The earth is cracking and I'm running away, so as not to be swallowed up!"

76

"Is that it?" cried the second Hare. "Dear me! Then I'll run away too!" and off he dashed beside her. Soon they met another Hare; they told him the earth was cracking, and off he dashed beside them. So it went on, till at last there were a hundred-thousand Hares all running away as fast as they could.

By and by the Hares met a Deer.

"Why are you all running so fast?" asked the Deer.

"The earth is cracking!" they wailed. "We're running away so as not to be swallowed up!"

"The earth is cracking? Oh, dear me!" cried the Deer, and she bounded after the crowd as fast as she could go.

A little farther on, they passed a Tiger.

"Why are you all running so fast?" called the Tiger.

"The earth is cracking!" the fearful ones wailed. "And we're running away so as not to be swallowed up!"

"The earth is cracking? Oh, dear me!" howled the Tiger, and he leapt away after the crowd as fast as he could go.

In a few minutes more, they met an Elephant.

"Why are you all running so fast?" asked the Elephant.

"The earth is cracking!" the fearful ones wailed. "And we're running away so as not to be swallowed up!"

"The earth is cracking? Oh, dear me!" trumpeted the Elephant, and he lumbered off after the crowd as fast as he could go.

At last the wise King Lion saw the animals running

pell-mell, head over heels in a crazy crowd, and he heard
them cry, "The earth is cracking!" Then he ran out
boldly before them and roared three times till they halted.

"What is this you are saying?" he cried.

"Oh, King!" they answered. "The earth is cracking!
We'll all be swallowed up!"

"Hoity-toity!" roared King Lion. "Let's take time
to find out if such a thing could be true. Who was
it that saw the earth crack?"

"Not I," said the Elephant. "Ask the Tiger! He told me!"

"Not I," said the Tiger. "Ask the Deer! She told me!"

"Not I," said the Deer. "Ask the Hares! They told me!"

So every single animal said he had not been the one to
see the earth crack and he pointed out someone else who

had told him all about it. When it came to the Hares, they pointed to the one foolish, timid, little Hare, who stood by shivering and shaking. "She told us," they all cried.

Then the Lion said, "Little Hare, what made you say the earth was cracking?"

"I heard it crack," said the Hare.

"Where did you hear it crack?" asked the Lion.

"By the big palm tree. I was fast asleep, and I woke up and thought, 'Oh, dear me! Suppose the earth should crack and swallow me up!' Just then I heard a cracking noise, as loud—as loud as thunder—and away I ran as fast as I could."

"Well," said the Lion, "you and I will go back to the place where the earth is cracking and see what is the matter."

"No, no, no!" cried the foolish, timid, little Hare. "I would not go there again for anything in the world."

"But," said the Lion, "I will take you on my back." So at last the foolish, timid, little Hare got up on the Lion's back and away they went like the wind, till they came to the Palm Tree. No sooner had they arrived than they heard a loud thud—the Monkeys threw down another cocoanut! And there they had the secret at last! At last the Hare understood how nothing but a falling cocoanut had made her think the earth was cracking. So the foolish, timid, little Hare went back to the other animals and said, "The earth is *not* cracking."

"Well! Well! Well!" said the Elephant. "You don't say! So the earth is *not* cracking after all!" And he lumbered off into the forest.

Thus every one of the animals went back into the forest, and that was the end of the earthquake.

The Right Time to Laugh

AN AUSTRALIAN TALE

IN A DENSE Australian thicket, a lyrebird scratching in the ground, once found a choice bit of food. So he spread his tail and rejoiced.

Just then along came a frog. "Good morning, friend," said the frog, and he sat very solemnly by, waiting to be invited to eat a share of the feast. But the lyrebird took his food and flew up into a tree.

"My friend," said the frog, feeling injured, "yesterday you dined with me, haven't you one morsel to spare for me today?"

"Certainly!" said the lyrebird, for he did not wish to appear so greedy as he was! "You may have a bite of my food. Just come right up and get it!"

"I can't come up," said the frog. "I've no wings with which to fly, and my feet were not made for climbing."

But the lyrebird, looking about, spied a vine trailing down from the tree with one end on the ground.

"Take hold of the vine," said he, "and I will pull you up." So the frog caught hold of the vine and the lyrebird pulled him up slowly until he was on a level with the branch where the lyrebird was sitting.

"I thank you, my friend," said the frog, and he was about to hop down beside the food he desired, when the lyrebird let go of the vine and dropped the frog—plump!—to the ground. Then the lyrebird, thinking he had played a very fine joke on his friend, laughed and laughed and laughed and he ate his dinner up all by himself.

But the frog was very angry. He sat down below and sulked, thinking of nothing but the trick which the lyrebird had played on him.

"Well, I'll pay him back!" the frog told himself. "I'll pay him back, I will!"

So he hopped to the neighboring river, where the lyrebird got his water, and he drank and drank and drank. He drank till he swallowed not only all the water in that river, but all the water in all the rivers and all the lakes in Australia! Then he sat, quite puffed out with the water he had swallowed, and solemnly blinked his eyes.

Soon the lyrebird wanted a drink; but where was he to get it? There wasn't a river to turn to! The lyrebird got thirstier and thirstier until he was half-crazy for want of a drink of water. At last he was sufficiently punished for the wicked prank he had played to be very sorry for what he had done. And alas! he wasn't the only one who suffered; for not a beast or a bird in all Australia could get a drink of water. One by one, they went to the frog and begged him to give out the waters. Dingo, the wild dog, went; Spiny, the anteater, went; Flying-fox, the great bat, went. And they said:

"Great frog, the lyrebird has done you wrong, but now he is very sorry and you are making us suffer who did you no wrong at all. Give forth the waters, we pray you."

But still the great frog sulked and would not answer a word. Then the lyrebird himself went before him and humbly begged his pardon. But the frog held, stubborn as ever, to the memory of his wrongs and he would not forgive the lyrebird. He sat as puffed up as before and solemnly blinked his eyes.

Then the great black swan went before him, and the white eagle, and the emu, and all the other birds and beasts. But no matter how they besought him, he would not give back the water. So at length the birds and the beasts all got together and said:

"If the old frog only knew how ridiculous he is sulking away like that, he would laugh at himself; then the waters would gush from his mouth."

"Ah!" cried the anteater. "If that is the case, let us *make* him laugh and give up the rivers."

So they all stood in a circle about the solemn old frog and performed their funniest antics. First, they brought out the duck-billed mole, and a funny enough fellow he was! They backed him up to the frog and from the mole's furry back, Mr. Frog expected, of course, to see the face of a beast. Then they turned the mole around quickly. Lo, there was the face of a bird with a flat, absurd bill like a duck's in the place where his snout ought to be! But the frog never smiled the least smile.

At last they brought out an eel, and that was a happy thought. The eel stood up on the tip of his long, long tail and he danced. He wiggled and wriggled and twisted. At that, the corners of the frog's mouth began all at once to turn up, his lips began to twitch, his nose began to wrinkle, and all of a sudden—Hah! He opened his mouth big and wide and he let out a mighty laugh. He laughed and he laughed and he laughed; and, as he laughed, the waters gushed forth from his mouth and filled up all the rivers and all the lakes in Australia.

"I was a silly old frog to sulk like that!" he cried.

Then the lyrebird, and the wild dog, and the anteater, and the flying-fox, and the opossum, and the black swan, and the white eagle, and the emu, and duck-billed mole, and the kangaroo all hurried to get the drink which they so sorely needed.

Little Half-Chick

A SPANISH FOLK TALE

ONCE there was a hen who made a nest for herself in a sunny farmyard in Spain. There she raised a brood of chicks. Fluffy and yellow and beautiful, they pecked their way out of their shells. Very good little chicks they were, too—all but one, that is—and he, dear me, dear me! When his mother called, "Cluck! Cluck! Cluck!" he never did what she told him. When she bade him come here, he went there; when she bade him do this, he did that! He snatched choice bits of food away from his brothers and sisters and he wanted his own way in all things.

One day Mother Hen noticed that this naughty little chick was really only a half-chick. He had only half a head, half a body, half a tail, one eye, one wing, and one leg!

"Dear me!" clucked Mother Hen. "What in the world is the matter? How did my chick ever come to be such a queer little fellow?"

But very soon it was plain even to good Mother Hen why this chick was only a half-chick. No matter how she tried to teach him to do what was right, he only tossed his half-head, flipped his little half-tail and did exactly as he chose. "Dear me!" said Mother Hen sadly.

One day Little Half-Chick came hopping up to his mother—stump, stump, stump on his one little leg.

"Good-bye, mother!" he said, "I'm off to the city to see the King!"

"Off to the city!" cried poor Mother Hen. "Why you haven't even learned yet how to behave in a farmyard! You'll never get on in the city. Stay here and learn from me, and, who knows, you may still grow to be a whole chick!"

But Little Half-Chick only tossed his little half-head and flipped his little half-tail.

"I know enough," he said, "without any teaching from you! Life here is too quiet for me! I'm off to see the King!"

And away he went, stump, stump, stump!

Over hill, over dale, on, on, hopped Little Half-Chick—stump, stump, stump, up the highway!

At length he saw a little brook, all choked up with weeds, that held it there a prisoner, so it could not laugh and run and go leaping on its way.

"Oh, Little Half-Chick," the water murmured, "the weeds have bound me fast. Please stop and pull them away that I may laugh and run."

But Little Half-Chick only tossed his little half-head and flipped his little half-tail!

"Stop and set you free!" he cried. "Why should I bother with you! I'm off to the city to see the King!"

And for all the brooklet's beseeching, he went on his way—stump, stump, stump!

A little farther along, what should he see but a fire whose flames were sinking down so that little of it was left, except a mass of red embers.

"Sticks! Give me sticks!" faintly sputtered the fire. "Oh, Little Half-Chick, feed me sticks or I shall go out!"

"Feed you sticks!" cried Little Half-Chick. "Why should I bother with you! I'm off to the city to see the King!"

And he tossed his little half-head and flipped his little half-tail and went on his way—stump, stump, stump!

Pretty soon he passed through a wood, and there he found the wind caught tight in a clump of bushes.

"Oh, Little Half-Chick, stop," faintly whispered the wind. "Pull these bushes apart. Let me out! Set me free!"

"Why should I bother with you! I'm off to the city to see the King!"

And Little Half-Chick tossed his little half-head and flipped his little half-tail and went on his way —stump, stump, stump!

By and by the road grew crowded with people going to town, some riding donkeys and some in wagons; and, in the midst of the crowd, Half-Chick slipped into the city and found the palace of the King. He stumped past a soldier on guard and into the palace yard. But, for all he thought he knew so much, he really knew very little. He didn't know the front door from the back door of the palace. So instead of going in the very grand front gate, he went in by a little back entrance that led to the King's kitchen yard. And just as he crossed the yard, the King's cook looked out of the window.

"Here's just what I need," he cried, "a chicken for the King's soup!" And he reached out the window, seized Little Half-Chick, ran with him to the fire, took the cover

off a great pot, threw in a handful of onions, garlic, toma-
toes, and peppers, and popped in Little Half-Chick! Then
he clapped down the cover, bang!

It was dark inside the kettle: the water rolled over
Half-Chick and twirled him round and round.

"Oh, Water!" cried Little Half-Chick, "do not twirl
me around! Help me! Help me! Help me!"

But the water began to bubble: "When I was in the
brook and could not run for the weeds, you would not
stop to help me. You would not set me free. What right
have you to ask me to stop and help you now?" And he
went on about his business of rolling around in the pot.

Soon the water began to grow hot.

"Oh, Fire! Fire! Do not cook me!" cried Little Half-
Chick. But the fire leaped up bright and crackled:

"When I was in need of
sticks, you would not stop
to help me. What right have
you to ask me to stop and
help you now?" And he
went on about his business
of making the water hotter.

Pretty soon the cook took
the cover off the pot to see
how his soup was doing.
As he stood there sniffing
its fragrance, who came a-
long but the wind.

"Oh, Wind, Wind, help me!" cried Little Half-Chick, "get me out of this pot! I pray you, get me out of this pot!"

"Ah, Little Half-Chick," the wind whistled, "when I was caught in the bushes, you would not stop to help me. What right have you to ask me to stop and help you now?"

But, just as the cook was about to clap down the cover again, the wind took pity on Little Half-Chick. He whisked him out of the pot, and he whisked him out of the window.

Up, up, up, he flew, high over all the roofs, high over the towers and steeples, up, up, up, over all the town.

"Only a little half-chick would act as you have acted," that was what the wind roared. "Here's the place for a little half-chick!"

And the wind dropped Half-Chick down bang on the very top of a steeple.

"There you are and there you stay," said the wind.

So Little Half-Chick at last found himself only a weather-cock. Fastened tight to the top of that steeple, he stands on his one little leg, even to this day, and he never has his own way, for he's twirled this way and that without even a by-your-leave, whichever way the wind blows.

UP ONE PAIR OF STAIRS

A PICTURE BY A LITTLE GIRL AND
A POEM BY A LITTLE GIRL
"There's Dozens full of Dandelions
down in the FIELD:
little GOLD pLATES,
LITTle GOLD DISHES IN THE GRASS.
I CANNOT COUNT THEM,
BUT THE FAIRIES KNOW EVERY ONE."

This poem was written by a little girl named Hilda Conkling when she was five years old, and she has written many more beautiful poems. Pamela Bianco was also a little girl when she drew this pretty picture. The poem is reprinted from *Poems by a Little Girl* by Hilda Conkling. Copyright, 1920, by Frederick A. Stokes Company. The picture is from *Flora* by Pamela Bianco. Courtesy J. B. Lippincott Company, Publishers, Philadelphia.

THE SWING

HOW do you like to go up in a swing,
    Up in the air so blue?
Oh, I do think it the pleasantest thing
    Ever a child can do!

Up in the air and over the wall,
    Till I can see so wide,
Rivers and trees and cattle and all
    Over the countryside—

Till I look down on the garden green,
    Down on the roof so brown—
Up in the air I go flying again,
    Up in the air and down!

—Robert Louis Stevenson

INDIAN CHILDREN*

WHERE we walk to school each day,
　Indian children used to play—
All about our native land,
Where the shops and houses stand.

And the trees were very tall,
And there were no streets at all,
Not a church and not a steeple—
Only woods and Indian people.

Only wigwams on the ground,
And at night bears prowling round—
What a different place to-day
Where we live and work and play!
　　　　　　　　　—*Annette Wynne*

*From *For Days and Days*, published by Frederick A. Stokes Company.

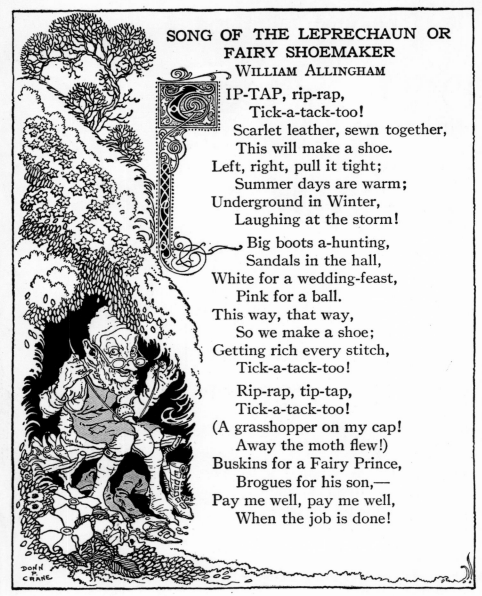

SONG OF THE LEPRECHAUN OR FAIRY SHOEMAKER

WILLIAM ALLINGHAM

IP-TAP, rip-rap,
  Tick-a-tack-too!
Scarlet leather, sewn together,
  This will make a shoe.
Left, right, pull it tight;
  Summer days are warm;
Underground in Winter,
  Laughing at the storm!

  Big boots a-hunting,
    Sandals in the hall,
White for a wedding-feast,
  Pink for a ball.
This way, that way,
  So we make a shoe;
Getting rich every stitch,
  Tick-a-tack-too!

  Rip-rap, tip-tap,
  Tick-a-tack-too!
(A grasshopper on my cap!
  Away the moth flew!)
Buskins for a Fairy Prince,
  Brogues for his son,—
Pay me well, pay me well,
  When the job is done!

94

UP ONE PAIR OF STAIRS

The Shoemaker and the Elves*

A German Folk Tale

ONCE there was a shoemaker who worked hard and was very honest; but still he was as poor as a church mouse and could not earn enough to keep himself and his wife. At last there came a time when all he had was gone except one piece of leather — just enough to make one pair of shoes. He cut out the shoes, ready to stitch and make up the next day, and he left them on his work bench, meaning to get up with the sun and start to work. Now the shoemaker was a good man, so his heart was light amidst all his troubles; and he went to bed, peacefully, trusting that he could finish the shoes the next day and sell them. Leaving all his cares to heaven, he laid his head on his pillow and fell asleep.

Bright and early the next morning, he arose and went to his work bench. Lo and behold, there stood the shoes, already made, upon the table! They were beautifully made, too; all was so neat and true, there was not one false stitch. Yet there was no sign of anyone's having been there. The good man and his wife knew not what to say or think. But the first customer, who came in, was so pleased with the beautiful shoes that he bought them. Indeed, he paid so much for them that the shoemaker was able to buy enough leather to make two pairs of shoes.

*In his *Elfin Dance*, the Norwegian composer, Edvard Grieg, has captured all the sprightly movements of elves. The Swedish folk music, *Shoemakers' Dance*, has been recorded for the phonograph.

95

The next evening he cut out the two pairs of shoes and went to bed early, as before. But, when he got up in the morning, there were the shoes on the bench, all finished and beautifully made, and, once again, there was no sign that anyone had been there.

That day in came customers who paid the shoe-maker handsomely for his goods, so he was able now to buy leather for four pairs of shoes. Once more he cut out the shoes and left them on the bench, and, in the morning, all four pairs were made.

And so it went on for some time, until the good man and his wife were thriving and prosperous. But they could not be satisfied to have so much done for them and not know to whom they should be grateful. One evening about Christmas time, as they were sitting over the fire and chatting together, the shoe-maker said to his wife: "I should like to sit up and watch tonight, that we may see who it is that comes and does my work for me."

The wife liked the thought, so they hid themselves behind a curtain and waited to see what would happen. Just as the clock struck twelve, two tiny elves came dancing into the room. They hopped upon the bench, took up the work that was cut out, and began to ply their little fingers, stitching and rap-ping and tapping at such a rate that the shoemaker was amazed and could not take his eyes off them. These little elves were quite naked, but they had wee little scissors and hammers and thread. Tap! tap! went the little hammers! Stitch! stitch! went the thread. No one ever worked so fast as those two little elves. They worked on until the job was quite finished and the shoes stood ready for use upon the table. Then they took hold of each other's hands and danced around the shoes on the bench. The shoemaker and his wife had hard work not to laugh aloud at the sight.

But, at daybreak, the little creatures danced away out the windows and left the room as it was before.

"These little wights have made us rich and happy," said the shoemaker to his wife. "How can we thank them and do them a good service in return?"

"I am sorry to see them run about as they do with nothing on their backs to keep off the cold," said the wife. "I should like to make them some pretty clothes. I should like to make each a tiny little pair of trousers and a tiny coat and a cap."

"And I will make each of them a little pair of shoes," said her husband.

That very day they set about it. The wife cut out two tiny pairs of yellow trousers; two weeny, weeny blue coats; and two bits of caps, bright orange (for everyone knows the elves love bright colors); and her husband made two little pairs of shoes with long, pointed toes. They made the wee clothes as dainty as could be, with nice little stitches and pretty buttons; and, by Christmas time, they were finished.

On Christmas eve, the shoemaker cleaned his bench and on it, instead of leather, he laid the two sets of gay little fairy clothes. Then he and his wife hid away as before to see what the elves would do. Promptly at midnight, they came in and hopped upon the bench to do their work; but, when they saw the little clothes they laughed and danced for joy. Each one caught up his clothes and put them on in the twinkling of an eye. Then they began to dance and caper and prance in a circle! But just as the sun rose, they danced out the window, over the green, and out of sight; and the shoemaker saw them no more. From that day on, all went well with the shoemaker and his wife and they never needed help anymore.

The Wee, Wee Mannie and the Big, Big Coo

A Scotch Folk Tale

ONCE upon a time when all wee folks were big folks and all big folks were wee folks, there was a wee, wee Mannie and he had a Big, Big Coo. Out he went to milk her of a morning. But the Big, Big Coo kicked up her heels and would not stand still.

"Hout! Look at that now," said the wee, wee Mannie—

"What's a wee, wee Mannie to do
Wi' such a Big, Contrary Coo?"

So off he went to his mother at the house.

99

"Mither," said he, "Coo won't stand still, and wee, wee Mannie can't milk Big, Big Coo."

"Hout!" says his mother. "Go tell Big, Big Coo she must stand still."

So off he went to the Big, Big Coo and said:

> "Big Coo canna' have her way.
> She must stand still! She must, I say!"

But the Big, Big Coo kicked up her heels, swished her tail, and would not stand still. So back went the Mannie to the house and said: "Mither, I've told Big, Big Coo she must, but she will not, and wee, wee Mannie can't milk Big, Big Coo."

"Hout!" says his mother. "Go get a stout, stout stick and shake it at Big, Big Coo."

So off he went and got a stout, stout stick. Then he shook stout, stout stick at Coo and said:

> "Big, Big Coo, ye must stand still,
> Or my stout stick I'll make ye feel."

But the Big, Big Coo kicked up her heels, swished her tail, tossed her head, and would not stand still. So back went the wee, wee Mannie to the house and said: "Mither, I've told Big, Big Coo she must, I've shaken stout, stout stick at her, but she will not stand still, and wee, wee Mannie can't milk Big, Big Coo."

"Hout!" says his mother. "Go to the draper's and get ye a gown o' silk, for to coax Big, Big Coo."

UP ONE PAIR OF STAIRS

So off he went to the draper's and bought a gown o' silk. Then he spread out the gown o' silk before Big, Big Coo and said:

"Hold still, my Coo, my dearie,
And fill my bucket wi' milk,
And if ye'll not be contrary,
I'll gi'e ye a gown o' silk."

But the Big, Big Coo kicked up her heels, swished her tail, tossed her head, lowered her horns, and would not stand still. So back went the Mannie to the house and said: "Mither, I've told Big, Big Coo she must, I've shaken stout, stout stick at her, I've coaxed her wi' a gown o' silk, but she will not stand still, and wee, wee Mannie can't milk Big, Big Coo."

"Hout!" says his mother. "Then go to Coo and soften her hard, hard heart. Tell her there's a sweet, sweet lady wi' yellow hair by the roadside, and she's weary wi' walkin', and weepin' for a sup o' milk."

So off he went to Coo and said:

"There's a lady by the roadside,
Wi' long and golden hair;
She's wearied out wi' walkin',
And weeps a-sitting there.

"'Twould make ye weep in buckets,
  If ye were just to think,
  She's weepin', weepin', weepin',
  For a drop o' milk to drink."

But the Big, Big Coo wept no tears in buckets for the lady by the roadside. She kicked up her heels, swished her tail, tossed her head, lowered her horns, bellowed out loudly, "Moo-oo, Moo-oo!" and would not stand still. So back to the house went the Mannie and said: "Mither, I've told Big, Big Coo she must; I've shaken stout, stout stick at her; I've coaxed her wi' a gown o' silk; I've tried to soften her hard, hard heart, but she will not stand still and wee, wee Mannie can't milk Big, Big Coo."

"Well, then," says his mother, "go to that Coo and tell her she *must not* stand still. Bid her kick up her heels, swish her tail, toss her head, lower her horns, and bellow out loudly, 'Moo-oo, Moo-oo!' Such a sair contrary beastie will never do aught but that which she thinks ye don't want her to do."

So off he went to Big, Big Coo and said:

> "Coo, ye darena' stand there still!
> Kick and rair—'tis what I will!
> Never dare to stand, I say,
> I bid ye kick and rair all day!"

When she heard that, the Big, Big Coo stood still, heels, tail, head, horns, voice, all still. Then the wee, wee Mannie milked the Big, Big Coo for the sweet, sweet lady with the yellow hair, and the Big, Big Coo never, never, acted like that again—till the next time!

103

A Quick-Running Squash

Alicia Aspinwall

CHARLES owned a garden. One morning his father called him and pointing to four stakes driven in the ground, said:

"All the land within those four stakes is yours, your very own. You may plant in your garden anything you like, and James will give you what you ask for."

The next day James gave the boy some seeds which he planted himself, James telling him how to do it.

He then got his watering-pot and sprinkled the newly-planted ground with warm water. Running across the lawn, he looked down the road to see if his father had not yet come from the village. His father was nowhere to be seen; but, coming down the road, was a most remarkable-looking man. He was tall and thin and had bright red hair which had evidently not been cut for a very long time. He wore a blue coat, green trousers, red hat; and on his hands, which were large, two very dirty, ragged, white kid gloves.

This wonderful man came up to Charles and asked for a drink of water, which he, being a polite boy, at once brought.

The man thanked him, and then said:

"What have you been doing this morning, little man?"

Charles told him about his new garden, and the man listened with much interest.

Taken by permission from *Short Stories for Short People*. Copyrighted by E. P. Dutton & Company, New York.

"Little boy," said he, "there is one seed that you have not got."

"And what is that?"

"The seed of the quick-running squash."

Charles's face fell.

"I don't believe James has that, and I don't know where to get one," he faltered.

"Now, as it happens," said the man, "I have one of those very seeds in my pocket. It is not, however, that of the common, everyday quick-running squash. This one came from India and is marvellous for its quick-running qualities. You have been kind to me, little boy, and I will give it to you," and, with a peculiar smile, this strange man produced from his pocket, instead of the ordinary squash seed, an odd, round, red seed which he gave to Charles, who thanked him heartily, and ran to plant it at once.

Having done so, he went back to ask when the quick-running squash would begin to grow. But the man had disappeared. Although Charles looked up and down the dusty road, he could see nothing of him.

As he stood there, he heard behind him a little rustling noise, and turning, saw coming toward him a green vine. He had, of course, seen vines before, but never, never had he seen such a queer one as this. It was running swiftly toward him, and on the very front was a round, yellow ball about as big as an orange! Charles, looking back to see where it came from, found that it started in the corner of his garden. And what had he planted in that corner? Why, to be sure, the seed of the quick-running squash, which the strange man had just given him.

"Well, well, well!" he shouted, in great excitement, "what an *awfully* quick-running squash it is. I suppose that little yellow thing in front is the squash itself. But indeed it must not run away from me, I must stop it." And he started swiftly down the street after it.

But, alas, no boy could run as fast as that squash; and Charles saw far ahead the bright yellow ball, now grown to be about the size of an ordinary squash, running and capering merrily over stones big and little, never turning out for anything, but bobbing up and down, up and down, and waving its long green vine like a tail behind it. The boy ran swiftly on.

"It shall *not* get away," he panted. "It belongs to me."

But that the squash did not seem to realize at all. He did not feel that he belonged to anybody, and he *did* feel that he was a quick-running squash and so, on he scampered.

Suddenly he came to a very large rock, and stopped for a moment to take breath, and, in that moment, Charles caught up with him and simply sat down on him.

"Now, squash," said he, slapping him on the side, "your journey is ended."

The words were scarcely spoken when he suddenly felt himself lifted up in the air, and bumpity, bump, over the stone flew the squash, carrying with him his very much astonished little master! The squash had been grow-

ing all the time, and was now about three times as big
as an ordinary one. Charles, who had a pony of his
own, knew how to ride, but never had he ridden anything
so extraordinary as this. On they flew—roll, waddle,
bump, *bump*, roll, waddle, *bang*—the boy digging his
knees hard into the sides of the squash to avoid being
thrown. He had a dreadfully hard time. Mount the
next quick-running squash you meet, and you will see
for yourself how it is.

To Charles's great delight, he now saw his father coming toward him, riding his big white horse, Nero, who

was very much frightened when he saw the boy on such a strange yellow steed.

But Nero soon calmed down at his master's voice and turning, rode along beside the big squash, although he had to go at full speed to do so.

"Gallopty-gallop" went Nero and "bumpity-bump" went the squash.

Papa lost his hat. (Charles had parted with his long before.)

"What are you doing, my son, and what, *what* is it you are riding?" asked his father.

"A quick-running squash, Papa," gasped Charles, who, although bruised, refused to give up the squash and was still pluckily keeping his seat. "Stop it! Stop it! Oh, do stop it!"

His father knew that this could be no ordinary squash, and saw that it evidently did not intend to stop.

"I will try to *turn* it and make it go back," he said; so, riding Nero nearer and nearer the squash, he forced it up against a stone wall.

But, instead of going back, this extraordinary squash jumped, with scarcely a moment's hesitation, over the high wall and went bobbing along into the rough field that lay beyond. But alas, before them was a broad lake, and as he could not swim, back he was forced to turn. Over the wall and back again over the same road he went and toward the garden whence he came, Charles still on his back and Charles's papa galloping at full speed behind them.

UP ONE PAIR OF STAIRS

The squash, however, must have had a good heart, for, when he reached the house again he, of his own accord, turned in at the gate and ran up to the wall of Charles's garden. There he stopped, for he was now so big that he could not climb walls and, indeed, had he been able to get in, he would have filled the little garden to overflowing, for he was really enormous.

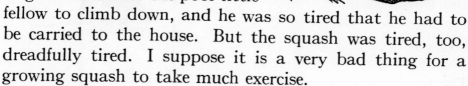

Charles's father had actually to get a ladder for the poor little fellow to climb down, and he was so tired that he had to be carried to the house. But the squash was tired, too, dreadfully tired. I suppose it is a very bad thing for a growing squash to take much exercise.

This certainly was a growing squash, and there is also no doubt that he had taken a great deal of exercise that morning.

Be that as it may, when the family were at luncheon, they were alarmed by hearing a violent explosion near the house.

Rushing out to see what could have happened, they found that the marvellous, quick-running squash had *burst!* It lay spread all over the lawn in a thousand pieces.

The family and all the neighbors' families, for miles around, had squash pie for a week.

THREE JOVIAL HUNTSMEN*

THERE were three jovial Welshmen,
    As I have heard them say,
And they would go a-hunting
    Upon St. David's day.

All the day they hunted,
    And nothing could they find
But a ship a-sailing,
    A-sailing with the wind.

One said it was a ship,
    The other, he said nay;
The third said it was a house,
    With the chimney blown away.

And all the night they hunted,
    And nothing could they find
But the moon a-gliding,
    A-gliding with the wind.

One said it was the moon,
    The other, he said nay;
The third said it was a cheese,
    And half of it cut away.

*Typical music of the hunt—spirited, full of the notes of the hunting horn, the barking of dogs, and the excitement of the chase—are *John Peel*, an old English hunting song; and "The Huntsman's Chorus" from *Der Freischutz*, by the German composer, Carl von Weber (1786–1826).

The Little Girl and the Hare
ADAPTED FROM WILHELM AND JACOB GRIMM

ONCE a woman had a pretty green garden with cabbages in it. But a little Hare came each day and ate the cabbages. Then the woman said to her little girl, "Go into the garden and chase the Hare away."

So the little girl said to the Hare, "Shoo! Shoo, little Hare! You are eating up all our cabbages."

Said the Hare, "Little girl, come, seat thyself on my little Hare's tail and go with me to my little Hare's house."

But the little girl would not go. The next day the Hare came again and ate the cabbages. And the mother said again, "Go into the garden and drive the Hare away."

So the little girl said to the Hare, "Shoo! Shoo, little Hare! You are eating up all our cabbages."

Said the Hare, "Little girl, come, seat thyself on my little Hare's tail and go with me to my little Hare's house."

But the little girl would not go. The third day the Hare came again and ate the cabbages. Then the mother said as before, "Go into the garden and drive the Hare away."

So the little girl said to the Hare, "Shoo! Shoo, little Hare! You are still eating up our cabbages."

Said the Hare, "Little girl, come, seat thyself on my little Hare's tail and go with me to my little Hare's house."

So the little girl seated herself on the little Hare's tail and the little Hare took her far, far away to his little Hare's house. When he reached there, he said, "Now you shall stay here forever, and be my cook and cook green cabbages and beans for me in the pot by the fire. I will ask some friends to come in and make merry with me."

The guests all came together. They were hares, and a crow, and a fox, and they stood out under the rainbow, waiting to be let in to the little Hare's house.

But the little girl was sad, for she wanted to see her mother. The little Hare came to her and said, "Open the door! Open the door! My guests are merry!"

The little girl said nothing, but she began to cry. The little Hare went away; then the little Hare came back again. He pointed to the pot and said, "Take off the lid! Take off the lid! My guests are hungry!"

The little girl said nothing but went on crying. The little Hare went away; then the little Hare came back again. And he said, "Take off the lid! Take off the lid! My guests are waiting!"

The little girl said nothing, but when the Hare went away again, she made a doll out of straw and dressed it up in her own clothes. Then she gave it a spoon to stir with, set it before the pot, and ran back home to her mother! The little Hare came once more and said, "Take off the lid! Take off the lid!"

But when the little girl did not take off the lid, the little Hare went up to see what was the matter. He poked the doll by the pot. Over it fell, its cap rolled off, and the little Hare saw that it was nothing at all but straw! So he had to open the door, let his friends in, and feed them all by himself.

THE HONEST WOODMAN

ADAPTED FROM LA FONTAINE*

A WOODCUTTER worked on the edge of a lake;
A poor man he was, with his living to make.
"The money I earn cutting trees," he would sing,
"Buys bread for my children! So ring, my axe! Ring!"

But once as he cut down a tree with a crash,
His axe-head flew off! 'Twas in the lake, splash!
The man sat down on the shore and he sighed.
"How now shall I feed my children?" he cried.

Then out of the water there rose on his sight
A beautiful lady dressed all in white.
And she said to him in a musical voice,
"I bring back your axe-head! Rejoice! Rejoice!"

He reached out his hand but, lo and behold,
What the lady held was a fine axe of gold!
"My axe was but steel! That's not mine!" he said.
She sank and the waters closed over her head.

*Jean de La Fontaine, who, like Aesop, is always associated with fables, lived at the court of Louis XIV, in France. He put French folklore and the popular tales of the Middle Ages into verse. His fables appeared from 1668 to 1694.

Still sadder he sat when she rose again.
"It may be that this is your axe then!"
"No, no! That's fine silver! It's not mine!" said he.
She sank again all ripplingly.

Like a fountain she rose. "Be glad!" said she.
"Here's your own steel axe! You shall have all three!
Since you would not take what was not your own,
You shall have all three for your loved ones at home!"

She sank, but the woodcutter made the woods ring;
He cut down big trees and he started to sing,
"My children, you shall be richly fed;
For an honest heart has won your bread!"

DOROTHY TODD

The Story of Li'l' Hannibal*
TRANSCRIBED BY CAROLYN SHERWIN BAILEY

Once on a time, 'way down South, there lived a little boy named Hannibal, *Li'l'* Hannibal. He lived, along with his gran'mammy and his gran'daddy in a li'l' one-story log cabin that was set right down in a cotton field. Well, from morning until night Li'l' Hannibal's gran'mammy kept him toting things. As soon as he woke up in the morning it was:

"Oh, Li'l' Hannibal, fetch a pine knot and light the kitchen fire."

"Oh, Li'l' Hannibal, fetch the teakettle to the well and get some water for the tea."

"Oh, Li'l' Hannibal, mix a li'l' hoecake for your gran'-daddy's brea'fus'."

"Oh, Li'l' Hannibal, take the bunch of turkeys' feathers and dust the hearth."

And from morning until night Li'l' Hannibal's gran'daddy kept him toting things, too.

"Oh, Li'l' Hannibal," his gran'daddy would say, "fetch the corn and feed the turkeys."

"Oh, Li'l' Hannibal, take your li'l' ax and chop some light wood for your gran'mammy's fire."

"Oh, Li'l' Hannibal, run 'round to the store and buy a bag of flour."

"Oh, Li'l' Hannibal, fetch your basket and pick a li'l' cotton off the edge of the field."

*Used by the courteous permission of *Good Housekeeping*.

Kemble

So they kept poor little Hannibal toting 'most all day long, and he had only four or five hours to play.

Well, one morning Li'l' Hannibal woke up and he made up his mind to something. Before they could ask him to light the kitchen fire, or fill the teakettle, or mix the hoecake, or dust the hearth, or feed the turkeys, or chop any wood, or go to the store, or pick any cotton, he had made up his mind that he was not going to tote for his gran'mammy and his gran'daddy any longer. He was going to run away!

So Li'l' Hannibal got out of bed very quietly. He put on his li'l' trousers and his li'l' shirt and his li'l' suspenders and his li'l' shoes—he never wore stockings. He pulled his li'l' straw hat down tight over his ears and then—Li'l' Hannibal ran away!

He went down the road past all the cabins. He went under the fence and across the cotton fields. He went through the pine grove past the schoolhouse, stooping down low so the schoolmistress wouldn't see him, and then he went 'way, 'way off in the country.

When he was a long way from town Li'l' Hannibal met a Possum, loping along by the edge of the road, and the Possum stopped and looked at Li'l' Hannibal.

"How do? Where you goin', Li'l' Hannibal?" asked the Possum.

Li'l' Hannibal sat down by the side of the road and he took off his straw hat to fan himself, for he felt quite warm, and he said:

"I done run away, Br'er Possum. My gran'mammy and my gran'daddy kep' me totin', totin' for them all the time. I doesn't like to work, Br'er Possum."

"Po' Li'l' Hannibal!" said the Possum, sitting up and scratching himself. "Any special place you boun' for?"

"I don't reckon so," said Li'l' Hannibal, for he was getting tired and he had come away without any breakfast.

"You come along of me, Li'l' Hannibal," said the Possum; "I reckon I kin take you somewhere."

So the Possum and Li'l' Hannibal went along to-gether, the Possum loping along by the side of the road, and Li'l' Hannibal going very slowly in the middle of the road, for his shoes were full of sand and it hurt his toes. They went on and on until they came, all at once, to a sort of open space in the woods and then they stopped. There was a big company there—Br'er Rabbit, and Br'er Partridge, and Br'er Jay Bird, and Br'er Robin, and Ol' Miss Guinea Hen.

"Here's Po' Li'l' Hannibal come to see you," said the Possum. "Li'l' Hannibal done run away from his gran'mammy and his gran'daddy."

Li'l' Hannibal hung his head like as if he was ashamed, but nobody noticed him. They were all as busy as ever they could be, so he just sat down on a pine stump and watched them.

Each one had his own special work and he was keeping at it right smart. Br'er Robin was gathering all the holly berries from the south side of the holly tree and singing as he worked:

"Cheer up, cheer-u-u!"

Br'er Partridge was building a new house.

Br'er Jay Bird was taking corn Down Below. You know that is what Br'er Jay Bird does all the time: takes one kernel of corn in his bill to the people Down Below and then comes back for another. It is a very long trip to take with one kernel of corn, but Br'er Jay Bird doesn't seem to mind.

Ol' Miss Guinea Hen was about the busiest of the whole company, for she was laying eggs. As soon as ever she had laid one she would get up on a low branch and screech, "Catch it! Catch it! Catch it!" like to deafen everybody. But Li'l' Hannibal was most interested to see what Br'er Rabbit was doing. Br'er Rabbit had on a li'l' apron, and he kept bringing things in his market basket. Then he cooked the things over a fire back in the bushes, and when it got to be late in the afternoon he spread a tablecloth on a big stump and then he pounded on his stew pan with his soup ladle.

"Supper's ready," said Br'er Rabbit.

Then Br'er Robin and Br'er Partridge and Br'er Jay Bird and Br'er Possum and Ol' Miss Guinea Hen all scrambled to their places at the table and Li'l' Hannibal tried to find a place to sit at, but there wasn't any for him.

"Po' Li'l' Hannibal!" said Br'er Rabbit as he poured out the soup. "Doesn't like work. Cyan't have no supper!"

"Catch him! Catch him!" said Ol' Miss Guinea Hen, but no one did it. They were all too busy eating.

They had a grand supper. There was breakfast strip, and roast turkey, and fried chicken, and mutton,

and rice and hominy, and sweet potatoes, and peas, and beans, and baked apples, and cabbage, and hoe-cake and hot biscuit, and corn muffins, and butter cakes, and waffles, and maple syrup.

When they were through eating it was quite dark, and they all went home, even Br'er Possum, and they left Li'l' Hannibal sitting there all by himself.

Well, after a while it began to get darker. Br'er Mocking Bird came out, and he looked at Li'l' Hannibal and then he began to scream, just like Ol' Miss Guinea

Hen: "Catch him! Catch him! Catch him! Catch him!"

Br'er Screech Owl looked down from a tree and he said very hoarsely:

"Who! Who! Who-oo!"

Then all the frogs began to say, loud and shrill, "Li'l' Hannibal! Li'l' Hannibal!"

So Li'l' Hannibal got up from his pine stump and he said, "I reckon I better go home to my gran'mammy."

Well, Li'l' Hannibal started for home, slowly, because his feet hurt and he was hungry. When he came to the pine grove by the schoolhouse the shadows came out from behind the trees and followed him, and that was much worse than seeing the schoolmistress. But Li'l' Hannibal got away from them all right. He crawled under the fence and ran across the cotton field and there in the door of the cabin was his gran'-daddy with a lantern. His gran'daddy had been out looking for Li'l' Hannibal.

"Why, Li'l' Hannibal, where you been all day?" asked his gran'daddy.

"Why, Li'l' Hannibal," said his gran'mammy, "here's your corn mush. I kep' it warm on the hearth, but afore you eat your supper, Li'l' Hannibal, jus' take your li'l' basket and run roun' to the chicken house for a couple of eggs."

So Li'l' Hannibal took his li'l' basket and he started off for those eggs, singing all the way. You see, he reckoned he was mighty glad to be at home and toting again.

UP ONE PAIR OF STAIRS

A Story About the Little Rabbits*

Joel Chandler Harris

"Fine um whar you will en w'en you may," remarked Uncle Remus with emphasis, "good chilluns allers gits tuck keer on. Dar wuz Brer Rabbit's chilluns; dey minded der daddy en mammy fum day's een' ter day's een'. W'en ole man Rabbit say 'scoot,' dey scooted, en w'en ole Miss Rabbit say 'scat,' dey scatted. Dey did dat. En dey kep der cloze clean, en dey ain't had no smut on der nose nudder."

Involuntarily the hand of the little boy went up to his face, and he scrubbed the end of his nose with his coat sleeve.

"Dey wuz good chilluns," continued the old man heartily, "en ef dey hadn't er bin, der wuz one time w'en dey wouldn't er bin no little rabbits—na'er one. Dat's w'at."

"What time was that, Uncle Remus?" the little boy asked.

"De time w'en Brer Fox drapt in at Brer Rabbit's house, en didn't foun' nobody dar ceppin' de little Rabbits. Ole Brer Rabbit he wuz off some'rs raidin' on a collard patch, en ole Miss Rabbit she wuz tendin' on a quiltin' in de naberhood, en wiles de little Rabbits wuz playin' hidin'-switch, in drapt Brer Fox. De little Rabbits wuz so fat dat dey fa'rly made his mouf water, but he 'member 'bout Brer Wolf, en he

*From *Uncle Remus, his Songs and his Sayings.* Used by permission of D. Appleton & Company.

skeered fer ter gobble um up ceppin' he got some 'skuse. De little Rabbits, dey mighty skittish, en dey sorter huddle deyse'f up tergedder en watch Brer Fox' motions. Brer Fox, he set dar en study w'at sorter 'skuse he gwinter make up. Bimeby he see a great big stalk er sugar-cane stan'in' up in de cornder, en he cl'ar up his throat en talk biggity: 'Yer! you young Rabs dar, sail 'roun' yer en broke me a piece er dat sweetin' tree,' sezee, en den he koff.

"De little Rabbits, dey got out de sugar-cane, dey did, en dey rastle wid it, en sweat over it, but twan't no use. Dey couldn't broke it. Brer Fox, he make like he ain't watchin', but he keep on holler'n':

"'Hurry up dar, Rabs! I'm a waitin' on you.'

"En de little Rabbits, dey hustle 'roun' en rastle wid it, but dey couldn't broke it. Bimeby dey hear little bird singin' on top er de house, en de song w'at de little bird sing wuz dish yer,

" 'Take you toofies en gnyaw it,
Take you toofies en saw it,
Saw it en yoke it,
En den you kin broke it.'

"Den de little Rabbits dey git mighty glad, en
dey gnyawed de cane mos' fo' ole Brer Fox could git
his legs oncrosst, en w'en dey kyard 'im de cane, Brer
Fox, he sot dar en study how he gwinter make some more
'skuse fer nabbin' un um, en bimeby he git up en git
down de sifter w'at wuz hangin' on de wall, en holler out:

" 'Come yer, Rabs! Take dish yer sifter, en run
downt' de spring en fetch me some fresh water.'

"De little Rabbits, dey run down t' de spring en try
ter dip up de water wid de sifter, but co's hit all
run out, en hit keep on runnin' out, twell bimeby
de little Rabbits sot down en 'gun ter cry. Den de
little bird sittin' up in de trees he begin fer ter sing, en
dish yer's de song w'at he sing:

125

" 'Sifter hole water same ez a tray,
Ef you fill it wid moss en dob it wid clay;
De Fox git madder de longer you stay—
Fill it wid moss en dob it wid clay.'

"Up dey jump, de little Rabbits did, en dey fix de sifter so 'twon't leak, en dey kyar de water ter ole Brer Fox. Den Brer Fox he git mighty mad, en p'int out a great big stick er wood, en tell de little Rabbits fer ter put dat on de fier. De little chaps dey got 'roun' de wood, dey did, en dey lif' at it so hard dey could see der own sins, but de wood ain't budge. Den dey hear de little bird singin', en dish yer's de song w'at he sing:

" 'Spit in yo' han's en tug it en toll it,
En git behine it, en push it, en pole it;
Spit in yo' han's en r'ar back en roll it.'

"En des 'bout de time dey got de wood on de fier, der daddy, he come skippin' in, en de little bird, he flew'd away. Brer Fox, he seed his game wuz up, en 'twa'nt long 'fo' he make his 'skuse en start fer ter go.

" 'You better stay en take a snack wid me, Brer Fox,' sez Brer Rabbit, sezee. 'Sense Brer Wolf done quit comin' en settin' up wid me, I gettin' so I feels right lonesome dese long nights,' sezee.

"But Brer Fox, he button up his coat collar tight en des put out fer home. En dat w'at you better do, honey, kase I see Miss Sally's shadder sailin' backerds en for'ds 'fo' de winder, en de fus' news you know she'll be spectin' un you."

THE DARING PRINCE
JAMES WHITCOMB RILEY

A DARING Prince, of the realm Rangg Dhune,
Once went up in a big balloon
That caught and stuck on the horns of the moon,
And he hung up there until next day noon—
When all at once he exclaimed, "Hoot-toot!"
And then came down in his parachute.

ROSY POSY

LAURA E. RICHARDS

THERE was a little Rosy,
And she had a little nosy,
And she made a little posy,
All pink and white and green.
And she said, "Little nosy,
Will you smell my little posy?
For of all the flowers that growsy,
Such sweet ones ne'er were seen."

So she took the little posy,
And she put it to her nosy,
On her little face so rosy,
The flowers for to smell;
And which of them was Rosy,
And which of them was nosy,
And which of them was posy,
You really could not tell.

128

Mrs. Tabby Gray
MAUD LINDSAY

MRS. TABBY GRAY, with her three little kittens, lived out in the barn where the hay was stored. One of the kittens was white, one was black, and one was gray just like her mother, who was called Tabby Gray from the color of her coat.

These three little kittens opened their eyes when they grew old enough, and thought there was nothing so nice in all this wonderful world as their own dear mother, although she told them of a great many nice things, like milk and bread, which they should have when they could go up to the big house where she had her breakfast, dinner, and supper.

Every time Mother Tabby came from the big house, she had something pleasant to tell. "Bones for dinner today, my dears," she would say, or "I had a fine romp with a ball and the baby," until the kittens longed for the time when they could go, too.

From *Mother Stories*. Used by the courteous permission of Milton Bradley Company.

One day, however, Mother Cat walked in with joyful news. "I have found an elegant new home for you," she said, "in a very large trunk where some old clothes are kept; and I think I had better move at once."

Then she picked up the small black kitten, without any more words and walked right out of the barn with him.

The black kitten was astonished, but he blinked his eyes at the bright sunshine and tried to see everything.

Out in the barnyard there was a great noise, for the white hen had laid an egg, and wanted everybody to know it; but Mother Cat hurried on, without stopping to inquire about it, and soon dropped the kitten into the large trunk. The clothes made such a soft, comfortable bed, and the kitten was so tired after his exciting trip, that he fell asleep, and Mrs. Tabby Gray trotted off to get another baby.

While she was away, the lady who owned the trunk came out into the hall; and when she saw that the trunk was open, she shut it, locked it, and put the key in her pocket, for she did not dream that there was anything so precious as a little kitten inside.

As soon as the lady had gone upstairs, Mrs. Tabby Gray came back, with the little white kitten; and when she found the trunk closed, she was terribly frightened. She put the white kitten down and sprang on top of the trunk and scratched with all her might, but scratching did no good. Then she jumped down and reached up to the keyhole, but that was too small for even a mouse to pass through, and the poor mother mewed pitifully.

What was she to do?

She picked up the white kitten, and ran to the barn with it. Then she made haste to the house again, and went upstairs to the lady's room. The lady was playing with her baby, and, when Mother Cat saw this, she rubbed against her skirts and cried: "Mee-ow, mee-ow! You have your baby, and I want mine! Mee-ow, mee-ow!"

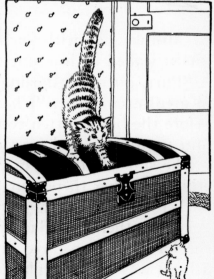

By and by the lady said: "Poor Kitty! she must be hungry," and she went down to the kitchen and poured sweet milk in a saucer, but the cat did not want milk. She wanted her baby kitten out of the big black trunk!

The kind lady decided that she must be thirsty.

"Poor Kitty, I will give you water," but when she set the

bowl of water down, Mrs. Tabby Gray mewed more sorrowfully than before. She wanted no water—she only wanted her dear baby kitten; and she ran to and fro crying, until, at last, the lady followed her, and she led the way to the trunk.

"What can be the matter with this cat?" said the lady; and she took the trunk key out of her pocket, put it in the lock, unlocked the trunk, raised the top—and in jumped Mother Cat with such a bound that the little black kitten waked with a start.

"Purr, purr, my darling child," said Mrs. Tabby Gray, in great excitement, "I have had a dreadful fright!" And, before the black kitten could ask one question, she picked him up and started for the barn.

The sun was bright in the barnyard, and the hens were still chattering there; but the black kitten was glad to get back to the barn.

His mother was glad too; for, as she nestled down in the hay with her three little kittens, she told them that a barn was the best place after all to raise children. And she never afterwards changed her mind.

THE KITTEN
AND FALLING LEAVES

SEE the Kitten on the wall,
   Sporting with the leaves that fall,
Withered leaves—one—two—and three—
From the lofty elder-tree!

   With a tiger-leap half-way
   Now she meets the coming prey,
   Lets it go as fast, and then
   Has it in her power again.
                        —*William Wordsworth*

133

Of a Tailor and a Bear

FROM THE MUSIC BY EDWARD MACDOWELL*

ONCE a tailor sat on his bench cross-legged as tailors sit and he stitched away on some cloth to make a suit of clothes. Now, this tailor loved his violin. He never was any happier than when he had his fiddle tucked comfortably under his chin. He would draw the bow across the strings, making sounds so deliciously sweet that they filled his soul with delight. And always when he worked, he kept his violin beside him.

Well one day as he sat stitching, he suddenly heard in the street a terrible commotion! What cries! What screams! What shouts! What a scurry of hurrying feet!

Looking up all at once, what did the tailor see, standing, big as life, in his doorway? There was a great, big bear who had broken away from his keeper and got loose in the street. The tailor was terribly frightened. A great, big bear coming toward him, lumbering on all four feet and growling as he came. What was the tailor to do? In a moment more the great creature would certainly be upon him.

Suddenly the man thought of his beloved violin. Bears liked music; he knew it. So he dropped the cloth he was stitching, seized his violin, tuned it, and started in to play. Never had his fiddle given out more beautiful music before.

*In this musical story by Edward MacDowell (American, 1861–1908), we hear the tailor at his work, then the commotion in the street, the appearance of the bear, growling, and his delight as he dances to the violin music.

And when the bear heard that music, he stopped right where he was. He came no nearer the tailor. He just stood up on his hind legs and started in to dance. Round and round he turned, slowly and very clumsily. His little eyes beamed with delight and he growled out his pleasure as he danced. And the tailor played and he played till all at once the bear's keeper, in a flurry of excitement, burst in at the door, seeking his wandering beast. He saw that all was well and the bear had done no harm. So he got him by his rope again and led the big creature away. The tailor laid down his fiddle and heaved a sigh of relief. Then he started in to whistle for joy and he made his needle fly as he stitched on his cloth again.

"Gr-r-r, gr-r-r, gr-r-r!" he could hear how the bear was growling as he went away up the street.

THE SONG OF SOLOMON

LO, the winter is past;
the rain is over and gone;
The flowers appear on the earth;
the time of the singing of birds is come.

—*The Bible*.

Oeyvind and Marit
(A Story of Norway)
BJÖRNSTJERNE BJÖRNSON

OEYVIND was his name. A low, rocky cliff overhung the house where he was born, fir and birch trees looked down upon the roof, and the wild cherry strewed flowers over it. On this roof lived a little goat belonging to Oeyvind; it was kept there that it might not wander away, and Oeyvind carried leaves and grass up to it.

From *The Happy Boy*. By permission of Houghton Mifflin Co. In Norway the peasants often cover their roofs with squares of turf in which grass continues to grow and from which even small bushes sometimes sprout, good pasturage for a goat.

One fine day, the goat leaped down and ran off to the cliff; it went straight up and soon stood where it had never been before. Oeyvind did not see the goat when he came out in the afternoon and thought at once of the fox. He grew hot all over, looked round about, and called: "Here, goat! Here, goat! Here, goat!"

"Ba-a-a!" answered the goat from the top of the hill, putting its head on one side and looking down. At the side of the goat, there was kneeling a little girl.

"Is this goat yours?" asked she.

Oeyvind opened wide his mouth and eyes, thrust both hands into his breeches and said, "Who are you?"

"I am Marit, mother's little one, father's fiddle, the elf in the house, granddaughter to Ola Nordistuen of the Heide farms, four years old in the autumn—I am!"

"Is that who you are?" cried he, drawing a long breath, for he had not dared to take one while she was speaking.

"Is this goat yours?" she asked again.

"Ye-es!" replied he.

"I like it so very much. Will you not give it to me?"

"No indeed, I will not!"

She lay flat on the ground staring down at him, and soon she said: "But if I give you a twisted bun for the goat, may I have it then?"

Oeyvind was the son of poor people; he had tasted twisted bun only once in his life, that was when grandfather came to his house and he had never eaten anything so good before or since. He fixed his eyes on the girl.

UP ONE PAIR OF STAIRS

"Let me see the bun first," said he.

She was not long in showing him a large twisted bun that she held in her hand.

"Here it is!" cried she, and tossed it to him.

"Oh, it broke in pieces!" said the boy, picking up every bit with the greatest care. He could not help tasting the very smallest morsel, and it was so good that he had to try another, till before he knew it, he had eaten up the whole bun.

"Now the goat belongs to me," said the girl.

The boy stopped with the last bit in his mouth. The girl lay there laughing, and the goat stood by her side, looking sideways down.

"Could you not wait a while?" begged the boy, his heart beginning to beat fast. The girl laughed more than ever and quickly got up on her knees.

"No, the goat is mine," said she and threw her arms about it. Then, loosening one of her garters, she fastened it about its neck. Oeyvind watched her. She rose to her feet and began to tug at the goat; it would not go along with her, and stretched its neck over the edge of the cliff toward Oeyvind. "Ba-a-a-a!" said the goat.

Then the little girl took hold of its hair with one hand, pulled at the garter with the other, and said prettily: "Come now, goat, you shall go into the sitting-room and eat from mother's dish." And off she went.

There the boy stood. He had taken care of the goat ever since winter, when it was born, and he had never dreamed that he could lose it; but now it was gone in a moment and he would never see it again.

His mother came up humming from the beach, with some wooden pails she had been scouring. She saw the boy sitting on the grass, with his legs crossed under him, crying, and she went to him.

"What makes you cry?"

"Oh, my goat—my goat!"

"Why, where is the goat?" asked the mother, looking up at the roof.

"It will never come back anymore," said the boy.

"Dear me! How can that be?"

Oeyvind would not tell what he had done at first.

"Has the fox carried it off?"

"Oh, I wish it were the fox."

"Then, what has become of it?" cried the mother.

"Oh — oh — oh! I happened to — to — to sell it for a twisted bun!"

As soon as he spoke, the boy understood what he had done, to sell his pet goat for a bun; he had not thought about it before.

The mother said, "What do you suppose the goat thinks of you, when you're willing to sell it for a twisted bun?"

The boy thought this over and felt perfectly sure that he could never be happy again. He was so sorry for what he had done, that he promised himself he would never do anything wrong again—neither cut the cord of the spinning wheel, nor let the sheep loose, nor go down to the sea alone. He fell asleep and dreamed about his goat. Then something wet was thrust right against his ear and he started up. "Ba-a-a-a!" he heard, and it was the goat that had returned to him.

141

"What! Have you come back again?" He sprang up, seized it by the two forelegs, and danced about with it as if it were a brother. He pulled it by the beard and was on the point of going in to his mother with it, when he heard someone behind him, and saw the little girl sitting on the grass. Now he understood why the goat had come back and he let go of it.

"Is it you who have brought the goat?"

She sat tearing up the grass with her hands and said, "I was not allowed to keep it; grandfather is up there waiting." While the boy stood staring at her, a sharp voice from the road above called, "Well!"

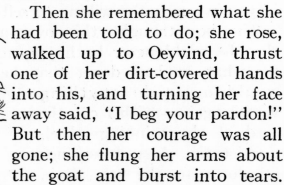

Then she remembered what she had been told to do; she rose, walked up to Oeyvind, thrust one of her dirt-covered hands into his, and turning her face away said, "I beg your pardon!" But then her courage was all gone; she flung her arms about the goat and burst into tears.

"I believe you had better keep the goat," stammered Oeyvind, looking the other way.

"Make haste now!" called her grandfather from the hill, so Marit turned and walked slowly toward him.

UP ONE PAIR OF STAIRS

"You have forgotten your garter," Oeyvind shouted after her. She turned and looked at him, then she answered in a choked voice, "You may keep it." He walked up to her, took her hand and said, "I thank you."

"Oh, it's nothing to thank for," she answered, but she still sobbed as she walked away.

Oeyvind sat down on the grass again, the goat roaming about near him, but he was no longer as happy with it as before.

The same summer his mother began to teach him to read. Then, one day, she said to him, "Tomorrow school begins again and you are going."

Oeyvind had heard that school was a place where boys played together and he was greatly pleased. He walked faster than his mother up the hillside, so eager was he. When they came to the schoolhouse, a loud buzzing like that from the mill at home, met them and he asked his mother what it was.

"It is the children reading," answered she.

On entering, he saw many children around a table; others sat on their dinner pails along the wall, some stood in groups around a large printed card covered with numbers. The schoolmaster, an old gray-haired man, sat on a stool by the chimney corner.

They all looked up as Oeyvind and his mother came in and the mill-hum ceased as if the water had been suddenly turned off. The mother bowed to the schoolmaster, who returned her greeting.

"I have come here to bring a little boy who wants to learn to read," said the mother.

"What is his name?" asked the schoolmaster.

"Oeyvind. He knows his letters and he can spell."

"You don't say so," said the schoolmaster. "Come here, little Whitehead."

Oeyvind went over to him; the schoolmaster took him on his lap and raised his cap.

"What a nice little boy!" said he and stroked his hair. Oeyvind looked up into his eyes and laughed.

"Is it at me you are laughing?" asked the schoolmaster with a frown.

"Yes, it is," answered Oeyvind, and roared with laughter. At that the schoolmaster laughed; Oeyvind's mother laughed; the children understood that they also might laugh, and so they all laughed together.

UP ONE PAIR OF STAIRS

When Oeyvind was to take his seat, all the scholars wished to make room for him. He, on his part, looked about for a long time. Then he spied near the hearthstone, close beside him, sitting on a little red-painted box, Marit with the many names. She had hidden her face behind both hands and sat peeping out at him.

"I will sit here!" cried Oeyvind at once, and, seizing a lunchbox, he seated himself at her side. Now she raised the arm nearest him a little and peered at him from under her elbow; forthwith he, too, covered his face with both hands and looked at her from under his elbow. Thus they sat cutting capers till the reading began again! The children read aloud, each from his book, high little voices piping up and lower voices drumming, while here and there one chimed in to be heard above all the rest. In his whole life, Oeyvind had never had such fun.

"Is it always like this here?" he whispered to Marit.

"Yes, always," said she.

Later, they too had to go forward to the schoolmaster to read; then they were allowed to sit quietly down again.

"I have a goat now myself," said Marit.

"Have you?" cried Oeyvind, and that was the very best thing he learned on his first day at school.

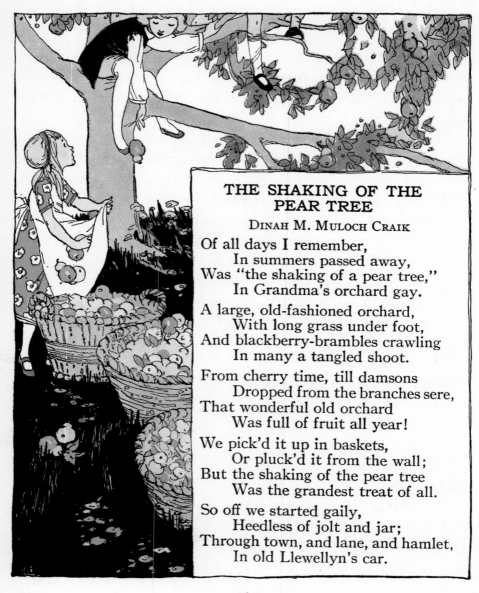

THE SHAKING OF THE PEAR TREE

DINAH M. MULOCH CRAIK

Of all days I remember,
    In summers passed away,
Was "the shaking of a pear tree,"
    In Grandma's orchard gay.

A large, old-fashioned orchard,
    With long grass under foot,
And blackberry-brambles crawling
    In many a tangled shoot.

From cherry time, till damsons
    Dropped from the branches sere,
That wonderful old orchard
    Was full of fruit all year!

We pick'd it up in baskets,
    Or pluck'd it from the wall;
But the shaking of the pear tree
    Was the grandest treat of all.

So off we started gaily,
    Heedless of jolt and jar;
Through town, and lane, and hamlet,
    In old Llewellyn's car.

The patient, kind Llewellyn—
    Whose broad face smiled all o'er,
As he lifted out the children
    At Grandma's very door.

And there stood Grandma's Betty,
    With cheeks like apples red;
And Dash, the spaniel, waddled
    Out of his cosy bed.

I hope no child will vex us,
    As we vexed Betty then,
With winding up the draw-well,
    Or hunting the old hen.

And teasing, teasing, teasing,
    Till afternoon wore 'round,
And shaken pears came tumbling
    In showers upon the ground.

O, how we jumped and shouted!
    O, how we plunged amid
The long grass, where the treasures
    Dropped down and deftly hid.

The Funeral March of a Marionette

The Story of the Music by

CHARLES FRANÇOIS GOUNOD★

ONCE there were some dolls who acted in plays to-gether in a little puppet theatre. These dolls were called marionettes and the man who owned the theatre had wires fastened to their arms and legs so he could make them walk or dance. Well, the man thought these mario-nettes were only wooden dolls. But that wasn't true. They were just like people. They were boys and girls and clowns and soldiers and nice old men and women. And when no-body was around, they laughed and talked to each other. Clackety-clack went their wooden tongues.

Now one of the boy dolls had a big plaid necktie, plaid trousers and a plaid cap of which he was very proud. But one night Sailor Boy snatched off Plaid Necktie's cap and threw it out the window. Then Plaid Necktie hit Sailor Boy—bang! And Sailor Boy hit Plaid Necktie. Bang, bang, bang! they banged. Louder, louder, they shouted! Noisier, noisier grew the fight! At last with one terrible *Bang!* Plaid Necktie hit Sailor Boy so hard that he fell to the floor all broken to pieces.

At that Plaid Necktie felt so bad he started to cry. And all the other dolls cried! They were all sad, so sad. And the Clown said:

"Now we'll have to take Sailor Boy to the Dump Heap for Broken Toys!" So they put Sailor Boy in a pretty box.

Charles Gounod (1818-1893) was a great French composer best known for his opera, Faust.

UP ONE PAIR OF STAIRS

They tied a ribbon around the box and stuck a rose in the ribbon. Then Plaid Necktie, the Clown and two other dolls took the box on their shoulders and they set out in a procession to carry the box to the Dump Heap. Slowly, slowly, solemnly, they went and their feet clacked in march time on the floor—*One*, two, *three*, four! *Slow*, slow, *slow*, slow! *Clack*, clack, *clack* clack!

Meantime, another marionette by the name of Soldier Man was sitting in a room that was quite a distance away. He and a friend were talking—chitterty chat! They were sip-sip-sipping nice cold lemonade when they saw that procession go out the front door.

"Oh my!" cried Soldier Man. "They're taking one of our comrades to the Dump Heap!" So the two ran off to join the procession. Hurry-scurry! Hurry! they ran! But when they caught up with the others they quieted down. Slowly, slowly, solemnly, they all went marching on—*One*, two, *three*, four! *Slow*, slow, *slow*, slow! *Clack*, clack, *clack* clack!

THE SEA SHELL*

SEA Shell, Sea Shell,
  Sing me a song, O please!
A song of ships and sailor-men
Of parrots and tropical trees;
Of islands lost in the Spanish Main
Which no man may see again,
Of fishes and corals under the waves,
And sea-horses stabled in great green caves—
  Sea Shell,   Sea Shell,
  Sing me a song, O please.
                    —*Amy Lowell*

*Used by the courteous permission of the author.

Clytie*

FLORA J. COOKE

CLYTIE was not always a sunflower, turning on her stem to watch the journeying sun.

Long ago she was a water nymph and lived in a cave at the bottom of the sea. The walls of the cave were covered with pearls and lovely pink sea shells. The floor was made of snow-white sand, and the chairs were of amber, with soft, mossy cushions.

On each side of the cave opening was a forest of coral and sea fans. Behind the cave were Clytie's gardens. Here she spent long hours taking care of her sea anemones, her star lilies, or in planting rare kinds of seaweed. Clytie kept her favorite horses in the garden grotto. These were the swift-darting goldfish and the slow-moving turtles.

*The wonder of sea caves is told in music in the overture, *Fingal's Cave*, by Mendelssohn, who visited Fingal's Cave off the coast of Scotland, in 1829. All the beauty of the sea, with its ever shifting waves, is also in *From Dawn Till Noon on the Sea, Frolics of Waves*, and *Dialogue of the Wind and the Sea*, by Debussy. This story of "Clytie" is from *Nature Myths and Stories*, copyrighted and published by A. Flanagan Company, Chicago.

For a long time she was very happy and contented. The sea nymphs loved Clytie, and wove for her dresses of the softest of green sea lace. They told her all their best stories. One day they took her to the mermaid's rock to hear the mermaid sing. Clytie liked one song best of all.

It told of a glorious light which shone on the top of the water. After Clytie heard this song, she could think of nothing else, but longed day and night to see the wonderful light. But no ocean nymph dared take her to it, and she grew very unhappy. Soon she neglected her garden and all her sea treasures.

In vain the nymphs begged her to forget the enchanting light. They told her no sea nymph had ever seen it, or ever could hope to see it. But Clytie would not listen, and to escape them she spent more and more of her time in her shell carriage, riding far away from her cave. In this way she could dream, undisturbed, of the glorious light which the mermaid called the "sun."

Now it happened that late one summer night, when the sea was warm and the turtles were going very slowly, Clytie fell asleep. Unguided, the turtles went on and on and up and up, through the green waters, until they came out at last close to a wooded island.

As the waves dashed the carriage against the shore, Clytie awoke. Trembling and filled with wonder, she climbed out of the shell and sat down upon a rock.

UP ONE PAIR OF STAIRS

It was early dawn, and the waking world was very beautiful. Clytie had never seen the trees and the flowers. She had never heard the birds chirping, or the forest wind rustling the leaves. She had never smelled the fragrance of the meadows, or seen the morning dew upon the grass.

She was dazed by all these wonders, and thought she must be dreaming, but soon she forgot all about them, for the eastern sky blazed suddenly with light. Great purple curtains were lifted, and slowly a great ball of dazzling fire appeared, blinding her eyes with its beauty. She held her breath and stretched out her arms toward it, for she knew at once that this was the glorious light she had dreamed about and longed for. This was the sun. In the midst of the light was a golden chariot, drawn by four fiery steeds, and in the chariot sat a wonderful, smiling King, with seven rays of light playing around his crown. As the steeds mounted higher and higher in their path, the birds began to sing, the plants opened their buds, and even the old sea looked happy.

Clytie sat all day upon the rock, her eyes fixed upon the sun with a great love and longing in her heart. She wept when the chariot disappeared in the West and darkness came over the earth. The next day from sunrise to sunset she gazed upon the sun,

153

and, at night, she refused to go home. For nine days and nights she sat with her golden hair unbound, tasting neither food nor drink, only longing more and more for the smile of the glorious King. She called to him and stretched out her arms, yet she had no hope that he would ever notice her or know of her great love.

On the tenth morning, when she leaned over the water, she was amazed, for instead of her own face, a beautiful flower looked up at her from the sea. Her yellow hair had become golden petals, her green dress had turned into leaves and stems, and her little feet had become roots which fastened her to the ground. Clytie had become the small image of the sun. The next morning, when she lifted her face to the beautiful light, it was so radiant with happiness that the great King himself seemed to smile back kindly at the happy little flower.

And so Clytie began her life upon the earth, and she became the mother of a large family of flowers with bright faces like her own. Her children are called sunflowers, and you may find them scattered all over the country, even in the dry and dusty places where other flowers will not grow. And if you care to, you may find out for yourselves whether or not it is true that all the sunflowers in the world turn upon their stalks, from sunrise until sunset, so that they may always keep their faces toward the sun.

THE SEA*

EMILY DICKINSON

AN everywhere of silver
    With ropes of sand
To keep it from effacing
The track called land.

*From *The Poems of Emily Dickinson*, Centenary Edition. Edited by Martha Dickinson Bianchi and Alfred Leete Hampson. Reprinted by permission of Little, Brown & Company.

155

The Babe Moses

RETOLD FROM THE BIBLE

ONCE there lived a great Pharoah who was the king over Egypt. Now he was a mighty king; but he was afraid in his heart because there lived in his kingdom a very large number of people who were not Egyptians. These people were the Children of Israel, who had come many years before from the rocky hills of the north and settled with their cattle and sheep on the green grasslands of Egypt. And Pharaoh was afraid that the Children of Israel would some day rise up against him and fight him and take away his throne. And Pharaoh said: "The Children of Israel are more and mightier than we are. Come on, let us deal wisely with them, lest it come to pass, when there falleth out any war, they join also unto our enemies and fight against us."

UP ONE PAIR OF STAIRS

And Pharaoh set taskmasters over the Children of Israel to drive them, with great whips, to heavy work in his brickyards and the building of his cities. And he made their lives bitter with labor in brick and in all manner of service in the field. But, in spite of all their sorrows, the Children of Israel flourished and grew mightily in numbers; for there were born unto them many sturdy babes.

So Pharaoh said: "I fear lest these Children of Israel should have too many boy babies that will grow up to be strong men and stand against us in battle. Come on then; let us throw into the river every boy babe that is born unto them."

Now there lived at this time in Egypt a man and his wife of the Children of Israel, and there was born unto them a boy babe, but he was a goodly child and his mother loved him and cherished him. And she kept him hid three months that Pharaoh's servants might not find him and throw him into the river.

And, when she could no longer hide him, she gathered bulrushes from the river bank and made of them a little ark. And she daubed the ark with mud and pitch and put her babe therein, and laid him in the rushes by the river.

Then she bade his sister stand afar off and watch what would be done to him. And she kissed the baby and left him and went back to her home; for she knew that God was with the child to save him.

And it came to pass that the daughter of Pharaoh, the King, came down to wash herself at the river; and her maidens walked along by the river's side. And, when the daughter of Pharaoh saw the ark among the rushes, she sent her maid to fetch it. And, when she had laid back the coverings, she saw the child; and behold, the babe wept! And Pharaoh's daughter was filled with pity and she said: "This is a babe of the Children of Israel, even such an one as my father has commanded should be thrown into the river."

UP ONE PAIR OF STAIRS

And she took the little one to her and held him in her arms. And she thought within herself that she would save this child; for she knew that the King, her father, would certainly grant unto her whatsoever she asked of him. So she cried to her maids and said, "I will ask of the King, my father, that I may keep this little one. He shall be as my own son."

Then came the sister of the babe, who had been watching by the riverside. And she said to Pharaoh's daughter, "Shall I go and call thee a nurse of the women of Israel that she may care for the child for thee?"

And Pharaoh's daughter said to her, "Go!"

And the maid went and called the child's own mother.

And Pharaoh's daughter said unto the child's mother, "Take this child away and nurse him for me, and I will give thee thy wages."

And the mother took her babe close. And she gave thanks in her heart that God had saved him for her.

And she nursed the child and he grew, and he lived with his mother and father until he was no more a babe. And when he was grown old enough to leave his mother's side, his mother brought him unto Pharaoh's daughter in the house of the King, and Pharaoh's daughter kept him as her own son.

And she called his name, Moses. "Because," she said, "I drew him out of the water."

When Moses grew to be a man, he gathered the Children of Israel together and led them out of Egypt where their lives were made so bitter. He led them to settle in Canaan, the land from whence they had come; and there they built their homes, and were happy once again.

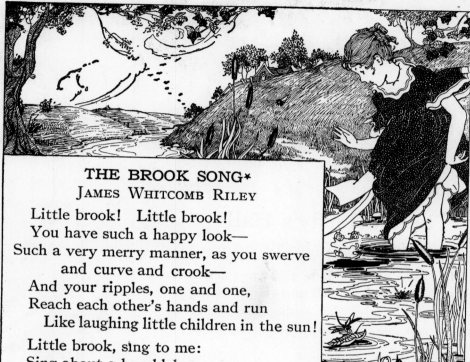

THE BROOK SONG*
JAMES WHITCOMB RILEY

Little brook! Little brook!
You have such a happy look—
Such a very merry manner, as you swerve
    and curve and crook—
And your ripples, one and one,
Reach each other's hands and run
    Like laughing little children in the sun!

Little brook, sing to me:
Sing about a bumblebee
That tumbled from a lily-bell and grumbled mumblingly,
Because he wet the film
Of his wings and had to swim,
    While the water-bugs raced round and laughed at him.

Little brook—sing a song
Of a leaf that sailed along
Down the golden-braided center of your current swift and strong,
And a dragon fly that lit
On the tilting rim of it,
    And rode away and wasn't scared a bit.

*Copyright used by special permission of The Bobbs-Merrill Company.

The Butterfly's Ball

An English Nursery Rhyme

COME, take up your hats and away let us haste
To the Butterfly's ball and the Grasshopper's feast!
The trumpeter, Gadfly, has summoned the crew,
And the revels are now only waiting for you!

On the smooth-shaven grass by the side of a wood,
Beneath a broad oak which for ages had stood,
The children of earth and the children of air
For an evening of fun, they all gathered there.

And there came the Beetle, so blind and so black,
Who carried the Ant, his friend, on his back.
And there came the Gnat and the Dragonfly too,
With all their relations, green, orange and blue.

And there came the Moth with her plumage of down,
And the Hornet with jacket of yellow and brown;
His companion, the Wasp, the Hornet did bring,
But they promised that evening to lay by their sting!

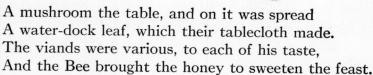

Then the sly little Dormouse peeped out of his hole,
And led to the feast his blind cousin, the Mole.
And the Snail, with her horns peeping out of her shell,
Came, tired out with traveling, the length of an ell.

A mushroom the table, and on it was spread
A water-dock leaf, which their tablecloth made.
The viands were various, to each of his taste,
And the Bee brought the honey to sweeten the feast.

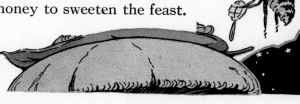

With steps most majestic the Snail did advance,
And he promised the others to dance a fine dance.
But they all laughed so loud that he drew in his head
And went in his own little chamber to bed.

Then as evening gave way to the shadows of night,
Their watchman, the Glowworm, came out with his light.
So home let us hasten while yet we can see,
For no watchman is waiting for you or for me!

LITTLE MAID OF FAR JAPAN*

LITTLE maid upon my fan,
  Did you come from far Japan?
What a tiny oval face!
Do you like this other place?

Do you miss the cherry trees
Where you know the little breeze,
Where you heard the cuckoo sing
In the spring?

Then you crossed your lattice floor,
Flung aside your paper door,
Joined the other maids at play,
Far away.

Now you live upon my fan,
Little maid of far Japan,
Still, you have a merry face—
Do you like this other place?

—*Annette Wynne*

*From *For Days and Days*. Reprinted by the courteous permission of Frederick A. Stokes Company.

The Tongue-Cut Sparrow*
TERESA PEIRCE WILLISTON

In a little old house in a little old village in Japan, lived a little old man and his little old wife.

One morning when the old woman slid open the screens which form the sides of the Japanese houses, she saw on the doorstep a poor little sparrow. She took him up gently and fed him. Then she held him in the bright morning sunshine until the cold dew was dried from his wings. Afterward she let him go, so that he might fly home to his nest; but he stayed to thank her with his songs.

Each morning, when the pink on the mountain tops told that the sun was near, the sparrow perched on the roof of the house and sang out his joy.

The old man and woman thanked the sparrow for this, for they liked to be up early and at work. But near them lived a cross old woman who did not like to be wakened so early. At last she became so angry that she caught the sparrow and cut his tongue. Then the poor little sparrow flew away to his home. But he never could sing again.

*From *Japanese Fairy Tales.* Published by Rand McNally & Company.

165

When the kind woman knew what had happened to her pet she was very sad. She said to her husband, "Let us go and find our poor little sparrow." So they started together, and asked of each bird by the wayside: "Do you know where the tongue-cut sparrow lives? Do you know where the tongue-cut sparrow went?"

In this way they followed until they came to a bridge. They did not know which way to turn, and at first could see no one to ask.

At last they saw a bat, hanging head downward, taking his day-time nap. "O, friend Bat, do you know where the tongue-cut sparrow went?" they asked.

"Yes. Over the bridge and up the mountain," said the bat. Then he blinked his sleepy eyes and was fast asleep again.

They went over the bridge and up the mountain, but again they found two roads and did not know which one to take. A little field mouse peeped through the leaves and grass, so they asked him, "Do you know where the tongue-cut sparrow went?"

"Yes. Down the mountain and through the woods," said the field mouse.

Down the mountain and through the woods they went, and at last came to the home of their little friend.

When he saw them coming the poor little sparrow

UP ONE PAIR OF STAIRS

was very happy indeed. He and his wife and children all came and bowed their heads down to the ground to show their respect. Then the sparrow rose and led the old man and the old woman into the house, while his wife and children hastened to bring them boiled rice, fish, and cress.

After they had feasted, the sparrow wished to please them still more, so he danced for them what is called the "sparrow dance."

When the sun began to sink, the old man and woman started home. The sparrow brought out two baskets. "I would like to give you one of these," he said. "Which will you take?" One basket was large and looked very full, while the other one seemed very small and light. The old people thought they would not take the large basket, for that might have all the sparrow's treasure in it, so they said, "The way is long, so please let us take the smaller one."

They took it and walked home over the mountain and across the bridge, happy and contented.

When they reached their own home they decided to open the basket and see what the sparrow had given them. Within the basket they found many rolls of silk and piles of gold, enough to make them rich, so they were more grateful than ever to the sparrow.

The cross old woman who had cut the sparrow's tongue was peering through the screen when they opened their basket. She saw the rolls of silk and piles of gold, and planned how she might get some for herself.

The next morning she went to the kind woman and said, "I am so sorry that I cut the tongue of your sparrow. Please tell me the way to his home so that I may go to him and tell him I am sorry."

The kind woman told her the way and she set out. She went across the bridge, over the mountain, and through the woods. At last she came to the home of the little sparrow.

He was not so glad to see this old woman, yet he was very kind to her and did everything to make her feel welcome. They made a feast for her, and when she started home the sparrow brought out two baskets as before. Of course the woman chose the large basket, for she thought that would have even more wealth than the other one.

It was very heavy, and caught on the trees as she was going through the wood. She could hardly pull it up the mountain with her, and she was all out of breath when she reached the top. She did not get to the bridge until it was dark. Then she was so afraid of dropping the basket into the river that she scarcely dared to step.

When at last she reached home she was tired out, but she pulled the screens close shut, so that no one could look in, and opened her treasure.

Treasure indeed! A whole swarm of horrible creatures burst from the basket the moment she opened it. They stung her and bit her, they pushed her and pulled her, and scratched her.

At last she crawled to the edge of the room and slid aside the screen to get away from the pests. The moment the door was opened they swooped down upon her, picked her up, and flew away with her. Since then nothing has been heard of the old woman.

THE MOCK TURTLE'S SONG*

Lewis Carroll

WILL you walk a little faster?"
said a whiting to a snail,
"There's a porpoise close behind us,
and he's treading on my tail!
See how eagerly the lobsters
and the turtles all advance!
They are waiting on the shingle—
will you come and join the dance?
Will you, won't you; will you, won't you;
will you join the dance?
Will you, won't you; will you, won't you;
won't you join the dance?

*In the story of *Alice in Wonderland* by Lewis Carroll, Alice went down a rabbit hole into a strange land where she met some very queer creatures, among them the Gryphon and the Mock Turtle, who sang her this song.

"You can really have no notion
  how delightful it will be,
When they take us up and throw us,
  with the lobsters, out to sea!"
But the snail replied: "Too far, too far!"
  and gave a look askance—
Said he thanked the whiting kindly,
  but he would not join the dance.
Would not, could not; would not, could not;
  would not join the dance.
Would not, could not; would not, could not;
  could not join the dance.

"What matters it how far we go?"
  his scaly friend replied;
"There is another shore you know
  upon the other side.
The further off from England,
  the nearer is to France,
Then turn not pale, beloved snail,
  but come and join the dance.
Will you, won't you; will you, won't you;
  will you join the dance?
Will you, won't you; will you, won't you;
  won't you join the dance?"

Lewis Carroll, an English professor, told the story of Alice for some little girls he took rowing at Oxford. In his *Looking Glass Suite*, Deems Taylor expresses in music the further adventures of Alice when she walked through the looking glass.

171

How the Brazilian Beetles Got Their Gorgeous Coats*

ELSIE SPICER EELLS

IN Brazil the beetles have beautiful, coloured, hard-shelled coats upon their backs like precious stones. Once upon a time, years and years ago, they had ordinary plain, brown coats. This is how it happened that the Brazilian beetle earned a new coat.

One day a little brown beetle was crawling along a wall when a big grey rat ran out of a hole in the wall and looked down scornfully at the little beetle. "Oh, ho!" he said to the beetle, "how slowly you crawl along. You'll never get anywhere in the world. Just look at me and see how fast I can run."

The big grey rat ran to the end of the wall, wheeled around, and came back to the place where the little beetle was slowly crawling along at only a tiny distance from where the rat had left her.

"Don't you wish that you could run like that?" said the big grey rat to the little brown beetle.

"You are surely a fast runner," replied the little brown beetle, politely. Her mother had taught her that a really polite

*Taken from *Fairy Tales from Brazil.* Copyright, 1917, by Dodd, Mead & Company, Inc.

UP ONE PAIR OF STAIRS

beetle never boasts about her own accomplishments.

A bright green-and-gold parrot* in the mango tree over the wall had heard the conversation. "How would you like to race with the beetle?" he asked the big grey rat. "I live next door to the tailor bird," he added, "and just to make the race exciting, I'll offer a bright-coloured coat as a prize to the one who wins the race. You may choose for it any colour you like and I'll have it made to order."

"I'd like a yellow coat with stripes like the tiger's," said the big grey rat, looking over his shoulder at his gaunt grey sides, as if he were already admiring his new coat.

"I'd like a beautiful, bright-coloured, new coat, too," said the little brown beetle.

The big grey rat laughed long and loud until his gaunt grey sides were shaking. "Why, you talk just as if you thought you had a chance to win the race," he said, when he could speak.

The bright green-and-gold parrot set the royal palm tree at the top of the cliff as the goal of the race. He gave the signal to start and then he flew away to

*The brilliant color of Brazil has inspired music as well as folk tales. "Thou Brilliant Bird" from the opera, *Pearl of Brazil*, by the romantic French composer, Félicien David, has all the flare and brilliant color of the parrot.

the royal palm tree to watch for the end of the race. The big grey rat ran as fast as he could. Then he thought how very tired he was getting. "What's the use of hurrying?" he said to himself. "The little brown beetle cannot possibly win."

Then he started to run more slowly, but every time his heart beat, it said, "Hurry up! Hurry up!" The big grey rat decided that it was best to obey the little voice in his heart, so he hurried just as fast as he could.

When he reached the royal palm tree at the top of the cliff, he could hardly believe his eyes. There was the little brown beetle sitting quietly beside the bright green-and-gold parrot. The big grey rat had never been so surprised in all his life. "How did you ever manage to run fast enough to get here so soon?" he asked the little brown beetle as soon as he could catch his breath.

"I flew here," said the little beetle.

"I did not know you could fly," said the big grey rat in a subdued little voice.

"After this," said the parrot, "never judge anyone by his looks alone. You never can tell where you may find concealed wings. You have lost the prize and the beetle has won it."

Then the parrot said to the little brown beetle, "What colour do you want your new coat to be?"

The little brown beetle looked up at the bright green-and-gold parrot, at the green-and-gold palm trees above their heads, at the golden sunshine upon the distant green hills. "I choose a coat of green-and-gold," she said. And from that day to this, the Brazilian beetle has worn a coat of green, with golden lights upon it.

THE BOASTER

ADAPTED FROM AESOP

A BOASTER boasted boastfully
He could do this and that;
His friends then said: "Sir Boaster,
Pray stop your silly chat!

"If you can do these marvels all,
No need to talk, my man;
Just *do* for us these wondrous things
That now you *say* you can!"

Chanticleer and Partlet

RETOLD FROM THE NUN'S
PRIEST'S TALE BY CHAUCER

ONCE a woman had a cottage near the woods and in a yard fenced round with sticks she kept a cock called Chanticleer. His feathers shone like gold, his bill was black, his comb was red. He was most beautiful to see. And not a cock in all the world could crow like Chanticleer. Each day he said good morning to the sun with one big Cock-a-doodle-doo-oo!

Now Chanticleer had seven hens but of them all he loved Dame Partlet best. She was so wise, so gay! Her manners were so good! They made a lovely pair when they went walking out together.

Well, Chanticleer was sleeping one dark night high up on a beam inside the hen-house. By his side sweet Partlet was asleep when all at once he groaned as if in pain. He groaned so loudly that he woke Dame Partlet up.

"My dear!" Dame Partlet cried. "What ails you? What's the matter? Tell me! What's the matter?"

Then Chanticleer, still groaning, woke up too.

"Oh, my love!" he cried. "I dreamed a dream! A bad, bad dream! I thought I was out walking in our yard when there I saw a beast! He seemed to be a dog and yet he was no dog! His fur was reddish yellow, his tail and both his ears were tipped with black. His snout was sharp. And, Oh, his eyes! They glowed like fire! He sneaked up on me as if he meant to seize me by the throat! And then I was afraid! I was afraid! I was afraid!"

"For shame!" Dame Partlet cried. "You! A cock grown up like any man! You should not be afeared as if you were a boy! A dream means nothing! Nothing!"

Then bold Chanticleer did truly feel ashamed.

"My love!" he said. "Now that I see you—how beautiful you are, how lovely those red lines about your eyes—it makes me feel so happy that all my fears are gone!"

By this time morning light had come, so Chanticleer flew down from his high perch and clucked to call the hens together. He strutted here, he strutted there! Like some great king he stalked about. He scratched the dust, he found some wheat. And then he clucked again so all the hens came running to eat the food he'd found.

> Royal he was; he was no more afeared.
> He looketh as it were a grim lion.
> And on his toes he roameth up and down;
> He deigneth not to set his foot to ground.

But while bold Chanticleer was bossing all the hen-yard, as proud as any king, a fox stole from the woods.

Nearby there was a garden where cabbages were growing. And there the sly fox hid, awaiting some good chance to fall on Chanticleer.

At noon the sun was shining and all the world was bright. Dame Partlet and her sisters were burrowing in holes to bathe themselves with sand. And Chanticleer was happy. Then he saw a butterfly. It flitted toward the cabbage bed and off he ran to chase it. But when he reached the cabbages and darted in among them, all at once he saw—Oh my! What did he see? He saw the fox, the beast that he had seen in dreams the night before! And now, he didn't crow! He couldn't say the smallest Cock-a-doodle-doo! He just said, "Cluck, cluck, cluck!" and turned to run away. But now the fox said sweetly:

"Oh, good sir, come back! Don't be afraid, for I'm your friend! I'd never do you harm! I only came to hear you sing! For I've been told your voice is like an angel's! Your mother and your father—bless their souls!—were both my friends! They used to visit at my house! And your good father—how that cock could sing! He'd stand up on his tiptoes and stretch his neck out long. Then he would shut his eyes and sing such Cock-a-doodle-doos as I have never heard on earth! Today, I did but come to learn if you can sing as he could! So I pray you, shut your eyes and let me hear you sing!"

And now when Chanticleer heard all those words of praise, he was afraid no more. He grew puffed up, he swelled his feathers out! And then at last he beat his wings with pride, he stood high on his toes, he stretched his neck, he closed his eyes, just as the fox had said his father used to do. With one triumphant crow he let out mightily a glorious Cock-a-doodle-doo-oo!

But while his eyes were closed the fox sprang up and seized him by the throat then bore him toward the woods.

All this Dame Partlet and the other hens could see. And now, in fear for Chanticleer, they let forth squawks and shrieks most terrible to hear while Partlet shrieked more loudly than them all. So great a noise they made the woman came a-running from the house. And so she saw the fox as he was making off with Chanticleer. Poor Chanticleer! The woman cried for help. She cried:

"Out harrow! Well away! Ha, ha, the fox!"

And when they heard that cry, men, women, boys and girls came running to her, some with sticks and some with staves. Dogs and pigs came too! Cows and ducks and geese! And they all ran after the fox!

Ran cow and calf and eek the very hogs,
So were they feared for barking of the dogs,
And shouting of the men and women eek;
They ran as though they thought their hearts would break!

But Chanticleer, for all that he was now held tight between the fox's sharp, sharp teeth, was thinking, thinking, thinking! Though his heart beat fast with fright, he was thinking how he might get away from the fox. At last he said:

"Friend fox, if I were you, a hunter bold, I'd never let those knaves chase, howling, all unanswered, at my heels!

I'd turn around and shout, 'A murrain take you all! In spite of you, I'll carry off this cock and eat him up!'"

Then Mr. Fox all filled with pride, cried out:

"You're right! I'll let those knaves know who I am!"

But as he spoke his jaws fell open and Chanticleer slipped out. Away he flew! Up, up, up, to the top of a tree he flew!

The fox stopped short! He gasped! How now? Had he been tricked? Aye, aye! But still he thought, "I'm smarter than that cock! I'll fool him once again!" So he cried out:

"Sweet singer, I was only teasing! I never meant to harm you! Come on down! We'll have some fun! Together, we can lead those howling knaves a merry chase!"

But Chanticleer crowed, "Nay! Cock-a-doodle-doo! You can't fool me again! Never again will I close my eyes and wink at what you do!

"For he that winketh when he ought to see,
God will never save from thee!"

Then the fox had to run for his life. But Chanticleer flew back to sweet Dame Partlet in the hen-yard.

A Happy Day in the City

OLIVE BEAUPRÉ MILLER

NED and his mother stood on the corner by the florist's shop waiting for the trolley car. Soon it came jangling up the track. Ned waved his hand to the motorman, and the big wheels squealed like a dozen little pigs as the car slowed down and stopped.

Ned had the money for their fare held tightly in his hand—he always gave it to the conductor himself. He and Mother stepped aboard; and, as the car started up with a jerk, they stumbled inside and made their way unsteadily to the only seat that was not already filled.

Oh, but Ned was happy! He loved to go downtown on the trolley car. He loved the bumping and the jiggling and all the wonderful sights. Today he was especially happy because he was going to meet his cousin, Ruth, and her mother, who lived in the country; and they were to have a long, beautiful day together in the city. He did not know what they were going to do to have a jolly time. Mother had kept that a secret, but he had seen Father slip out of the front door very quickly and mysteriously that morning as if he were carrying something; and he guessed—but, then he only guessed, he didn't really know, because it was a secret.

"When I grow up," cried Ned, as their motorman clanged his bell loudly, "I'm going to be a motorman!"

"Oh!" said his mother, "I thought you said yesterday you wanted to be a hurdy-gurdy man and have a street piano and a monkey."

"No!" announced Ned positively, "I'm going to be a motorman, and bang my foot down on the bell and make a big noise—clang, clang! And all the people will run to get out of the way of my car!"

So they went on for almost an hour, past apartment houses and little uptown stores, right into the hurly-burly of downtown. Then Mother pressed a button beside their seat to let the conductor know they wanted to get off. The car stopped, and they stepped down on a crowded crossing among automobiles and people, right under the tall iron framework where an elevated train rushed by with a roaring, rumbling noise overhead.

Next they walked over to the station where Ruth's train would be coming from the country. They crossed the clean, marble-paved floor of the station and went up the broad stairs to the place where the trains came

The beauty of the country has long inspired poets, artists, and musicians, but only modern poets and composers have found beauty in the city. *Skyscrapers* by John Alden Carpenter is a ballet of the modern city.

UP ONE PAIR OF STAIRS

in. A great iron fence shut off the tracks from the rest of the station, but a guard in blue uniform was already opening the gate to the platform where Ruth's train was pulling in, and a number of people were crowding about to meet friends whom they were expecting.

"Oh, I see her! I see her!" piped Ned. "And there's Aunt Frances, too!" Sure enough! There they were, coming along in the midst of the crowd. Soon everybody was kissing everybody else, and Ruth was telling Ned about her new kittens, and the garden she had made, and how she could read in her primer, all at once.

"Where are we going today?" asked Ruth.

"Oh, that's going to be a s'prise! You mustn't ask," said Ned.

"But I want to know," insisted Ruth, who never could wait for a surprise.

"Well this morning I saw Father slip out the front door and I'm almost sure he was carrying . . . .!" But there Ned stopped, smiling mysteriously, and he would not say another word.

Mother and Aunt Frances started on ahead, talking, with the children following behind them. They went down a long flight of stairs and out-of-doors to a place where they all climbed up into a bus and now they were off for the big stores uptown. But they had only gone a little way when, all at once, they heard a loud alarm bell ringing, and the bus suddenly stopped. Ruth and Ned turned around and looked excitedly out of the window.

Adventures in a Perambulator by John Alden Carpenter is a child's impression of the city. Jazz, like Carpenter's music, with its tricks of accent and rhythm, its color and variety of tone and volume, well suits the city.

They had just come to the bridge over the river, and, as the bell kept on ringing, people were hurrying and scurrying to get across. No sooner was the bridge empty than a chain was stretched over the approach to it, and a big policeman took his place there to prevent anyone else from stepping on it. Then the huge structure parted in the middle, and the two sides were raised straight up in the air by machinery from a little house on shore.

Next, a great steamer with tall funnels—too tall to have passed under the bridge when it was down—was pulled by a little puffing, smoking tug slowly past the crossing; and the little tug whistled shrilly for the next bridge up river to open out of its way.

UP ONE PAIR OF STAIRS

"Oh, Ned!" cried Ruth, as she watched all this with breathless interest, "I wonder how it would be if any-body would just hang on to the bridge and swing right up with it into the air?"

"Well," laughed Mother, "unless 'anybody' was a fly, I think 'anybody' would not hang on very long."

"Splash! He'd go into the water," said Ned, "and we'd have to fish him out."

When the bridge was down again, the bus went jiggling and joggling on, till it came to a great store where everybody got out. The store took up a whole block and was many, many stories high. All about were buildings so tall that the street seemed only a narrow slit between them. The bigness of those buildings made Ruth feel small and lonely; so she came nearer to Ned and took fast hold of his hand. But that wasn't the way the big buildings made Ned feel at all.

"When I get big," he cried, "I'm going to be a builder, and build way, way up till I can touch the sky!" As he looked up to think how very high he was going to build, he stubbed his toe and fell flat on the sidewalk, pulling Ruth half-way down with him.

"My dear little boy," laughed his mother as she helped him up and brushed him off, "before you can build to the sky, you will have to learn to look where you take your next step!"

All the buildings around were gray—all turned a soft,

An American in Paris, by George Gershwin, is a musical picture of the city, its noises, bustle, and confusion. It is American composers like Gershwin and Carpenter who have really felt the thrill of the big city.

pearly gray by the city smoke. Everything was gray except the bright colored signboards hanging high up in the air, and the gay things in the shop windows.

Mother and Aunt Frances and Ned and Ruth walked into the great store. There were many people inside, but the store was so large it did not seem crowded.

There were any number of counters about, covered with lace and ribbons and gloves and handkerchiefs and many other things; and, in one place, there was an opening in the ceiling, four or five stories high. To look way way up so far, almost took Ned's breath away. And there way up at the top, the roof of the great opening was a dome made of colored glass that shone and glittered like jewels. "Just like the castles in fairy land," said Ruth.

Mother and Aunt Frances stopped at the lace counter and the ribbon counter and the glove counter. It wasn't very interesting looking at those things; and Ned was stooping down looking in the lower part of the glass showcase where the buttons were—entertaining himself with thinking what fine wheels for his trains some of the big buttons would make—when, all of a sudden, Aunt Frances turned around to look for Ruth. She wasn't there at all! She had disappeared! There wasn't a sign of her anywhere to be seen!

Aunt Frances called her, but she did not answer; not one of the saleswomen had noticed where she went, and neither had the big, important floorwalkers. So Mother, Ned, and Aunt Frances hunted and hunted; and, at last, they found her a long way off looking at a pile of little girls' parasols, and half-covered up by a yellow one that she had opened over her head.

"Why, Ruth Maxwell Martin!" said her mother. "We've been hunting fifteen minutes for you. You're a big enough little girl to know you must not wander away."

Ruth hung her head and looked foolish, but Mother knew how much she wanted the little yellow umbrella; so she bought it for her and Ruth stood under it looking like the happiest little girl in town.

Then Aunt Frances said, "Most of our shopping isn't very interesting to the children. Let's leave them for an hour in the playroom."

So they all crossed over to a row of elevators, and they got into one with a great crowd of other people and they went up to the fourth floor. Then they passed through the beautiful toy section and they saw all the dolls and the dolls' houses and dolls' furniture and dolls' clothes. And they saw the toy animals and the toy villages and the toy automobiles and the toy aeroplanes and toy trains, that would really run by electricity; and they saw toy stoves, that would really cook by electricity; and oh, such a number of other things, that Ruth let out a big sigh.

"I wish I could *live* in a place like this!" she said.

"Well, you can live here for an hour," laughed her mother, as they went on into the playroom. A great number of children were there, laughing and chattering, playing in sand-boxes, sliding down wooden slides, rocking back and

forth on great horses as big as life, riding on little merry-go-rounds, or swinging in the swings. Ned and Ruth had time to try everything that was fun in the whole place before their mothers came back again to get them.

When they all started out once more, the hands of the big clock above the elevators pointed to twelve o'clock; so they went into the nice, clean, white marble washroom and got ready for lunch. Then they went up to the restaurant. The room, where they ate, had a beautiful fountain in the center with gold fish swimming in it. Ned and Ruth watched the fish dart around and could hardly bear to leave them even to order lunch. They sat down at a table that had a white cloth on it and a candlestick with a pretty pink shade in the centre; and, pretty soon, a neat young woman in black, wearing a nice white

188

apron, came and brought Mother and Aunt Frances each a card that had a list of all the good things they might have to eat. She took their order and went off; and, when she came back, her big tray was loaded. There was some orange and banana salad in a pretty nest of lettuce for each of those hungry people. There were lots of buns covered with sugar and currants, and four little bottles of milk. For dessert they each had chocolate ice-cream.

"Oh, I'm having *such* a good time!" said Ruth. "But Ned says it's a secret where we were going this afternoon. I just do wish I knew."

"Well," said Mother, "I'll tell you, Ruth. We're all going home and take a nap!"

"Oh, no, no, no!" shrieked both children.

After lunch they left the big store, and came out on

the crowded street. Such a number of people as there were, all busily hurrying somewhere! There wasn't any lingering here. Everybody had something to do and was keeping right about his business of getting there to do it.

In the street, there seemed a tangled mass of automobiles and people. But there was a policeman on the corner and, when Ruth and Ned reached there, they saw that what had seemed such a tangled mass was very orderly after all. When the policeman blew his whistle and held up his hand, all the automobiles and all the people going in one direction started up while the others waited. And, when he whistled again, those going in the other direction were off, so they never interfered with each other.

"When I grow up, I'm going to be a big policeman," said Ned.

"Then you'll hold up your hand and make all the automobiles and all the people wait while I cross the street, won't you?" said Ruth.

Soon they came to the wide boulevard where were all the finest small shops in the city. On the farther side of the street was a pretty strip of green park with shrubbery, flowers, and statues, that stretched all the way up the avenue; and beyond that strip, sparkled the blue waters of the lake. But Ned, Ruth, Mother, and Aunt Frances were chiefly interested in the windows of the shops on their own side of the street as they walked along. Ned stopped in front of the electrical shop where there were washing machines and fans and a little toy train all running by electricity. Ruth lingered by the big waxen figures of ladies dressed in such beautiful clothes that they seemed like princesses out of a fairy tale. Mother and Aunt Frances looked in at the linen and jewelry, and they all stopped together to peep at the candy and the flowers.

"I know where we're going," whispered Ned to Ruth. "To Father's office!"

Sure enough. They went into a large office building, rode up in the elevator, and walked down a long hall into Father's office. There was Father working busily at his desk.

"Well, hello!" he cried, as he whirled round in his chair, kissed Ruth, put his arm around Ned, shook hands with Aunt Frances, and smiled at Mother.

"Oh, Uncle," cried Ruth, "please tell me, where are we going this afternoon?"

But Father wouldn't tell either. He just smiled and left the room. While they were waiting for him to come back, the children went over to the window and looked out. They were up very high and the people and automobiles in the street below looked very small.

Near by, on the other side of the street, was a great stone building with two fine bronze lions, on either side of the broad steps, guarding the entrance. And, in the carved border about the roof of the building where Ruth and Ned could see them clearly, a number of pigeons roosted; while others flew circling about in the air or dropped down into the park below to bathe and play in the waters of the fountain. Farther on, beyond the green stretch of parkway, they could just see the tops of trains on a track down below the level of the ground. From the engines, rose little white curls of smoke that floated away and melted into the soft haze hanging over the lake beyond. Sometimes the sunlight pierced the haze and flashed back brightly from the water, from the white sail of a boat, or the wing of a great white bird. It was all very soft and lovely.

In a few moments, back came Father; and, there, the children saw he had the big picnic basket over his arm.

"Oh, Uncle, where are we going?" cried Ruth.

"Goody! Goody! A picnic! I thought so!" piped Ned.

"How will Lincoln Park do?" asked Father.

Soon they had climbed to the top of a bus from which

they could see everything as they rolled along down the boulevard, past rows of handsome houses.

At last they came into a park and passed a little harbor where a number of launches were anchored. Then they got off the bus beside a pretty knoll with a fine view over the lake. There, beneath a tree, Mother and Aunt Frances sat on a bench to rest while Father put the lunch basket down and took the children to the zoo to see the animals and birds.

In the birdhouse there was such a screeching, they could hardly hear themselves think; and in the cages round about, there was every kind of strange bird. Some were long-legged, some were short-legged, and some were queer, indeed. One old pelican, strutting proudly around the pool seemed to think he owned the place.

"When you grow up, Ned, how would you like to be a pelican?" asked Father with a twinkle in his eye.

They walked on past the zebras, the llamas, the camels, and the buffaloes; and they came back by the pits of the bears, the foxes, and the wolves. They saw the giraffes eating hay out of a high trough, and the elephant swinging his trunk. They spent a long time laughing at the antics of the monkeys; and, last of all, they visited the great house where the lions, tigers, and leopards were kept.

"I'd like to see a real wild tiger prowling around in the jungle," said Ned.

"Oh, dear! I shouldn't!" said Ruth. "What would you do, Ned, if you did see one?"

"I think," answered Father very solemnly, "that Ned

would run after the lion like a brave man and sprinkle salt on his tail!''

By the time they got back to Mother and Aunt Frances, it was time to eat supper. Lots of other people were picnicking nearby with goodies all spread out on table cloths on the grass. Children were romping and playing and some were wading in the lake. Before they knew it, supper was all spread out on the grass. My, how good that supper tasted out in the beautiful park!

It was growing dusk and the little Japanese lanterns were lit when Aunt Frances said, "Now, Ruthie, we must start for home, or you'll never be able to keep your eyes open until we get on the train."

So Father hailed a bus and they all climbed up on top and started off for home. Ruth and Ned were so tired, after all they'd done that day, that they just sat and grinned at each other. They never said a single word, but they kept thinking just the same, "What a good time we had today!"

CITY SMOKE
OLIVE BEAUPRÉ MILLER

From
    tall
        black
            chimneys
      leaps the
     smoke;
   Climbs high
     the drifting
       ladder
         of the
            wind;

Leaves far behind
    the chasing flames
       that mount the sky to catch it;
      Laughs out its joy in
        soft, white puffs;

Then slowly fades to pearl and purple,
And, settling to the earth,
   Outspreads o'er all the city
     Its brooding, dove-gray wings!

The Wind and the Sun

THE Wind and the Sun once met,
And together they made a bet.
Said the Wind: "Over there, there's a man—
I can blow his cloak off, I can!
That's something I'll bet you can't do,
I'll prove I'm more powerful than you!"
He blustered and roared as he spoke.
The man shivered and drew close his cloak.

And the fiercer the fierce Wind blew,
The closer that cloak the man drew.
Then the Sun, glowing soft and mild,
Shone warmly and gently and smiled.
And as he grew warm—what a joke!
The man took off his cloak!
Then the Sun said, "Smiles can do more
Than all the Wind's bluster and roar!"

—*Adapted from Aesop's Fables*

These illustrations are modeled on those of Walter Crane, one of the greatest English illustrators of the late 19th Century. His beautifully decorative drawings have left a great influence on the art of our time in its love for decoration and design.

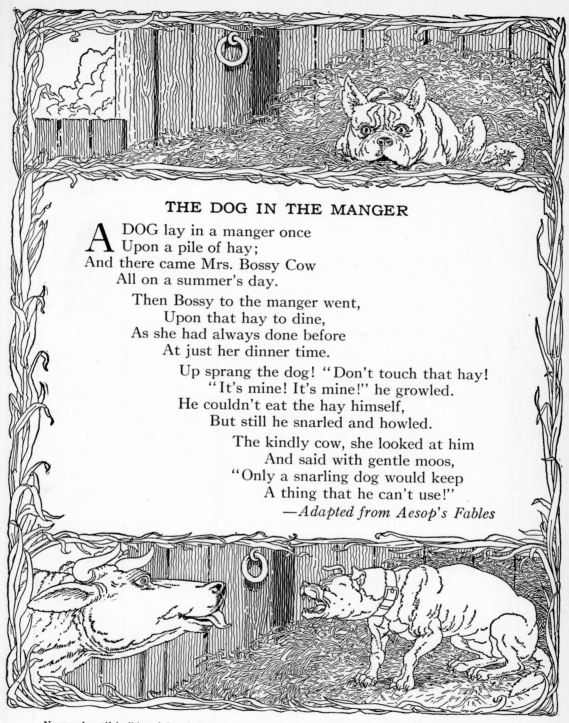

THE DOG IN THE MANGER

A DOG lay in a manger once
　　Upon a pile of hay;
And there came Mrs. Bossy Cow
　　All on a summer's day.

Then Bossy to the manger went,
　　Upon that hay to dine,
As she had always done before
　　At just her dinner time.

Up sprang the dog! "Don't touch that hay!
　　"It's mine! It's mine!" he growled.
He couldn't eat the hay himself,
　　But still he snarled and howled.

The kindly cow, she looked at him
　　And said with gentle moos,
"Only a snarling dog would keep
　　A thing that he can't use!"

—*Adapted from Aesop's Fables*

No more beautiful edition of *Aesop's Fables* has ever appeared than that illustrated by Crane—*A Baby's Own Aesop*. Picture books by such masters of illustration as Crane, Caldecott, and Kate Greenaway belong in every child's library.

The Birds' St. Valentine's Day
Retold from The Parlement of Foules
GEOFFREY CHAUCER

ON St. Valentine's Day Mother Nature calls all the birds together to choose their mates. Once they gathered on a fresh green meadow by a river. All around them fruit trees were in bloom and on a little hill good Mother Nature sat. Flowers grew all about her. In the river little fishes swam; they whisked their fins and shone like silver. Rabbits skipped and on the branches of the trees the birds were singing. For good St. Valentine had driven away the winter. And all the birds were singing:

"Spring is here! It's here! It's here!"

Then came flying through the air a little elf called Cupid. He was shooting magic arrows. And when the birds felt in their hearts those magic arrows they were filled with love and each one wished to choose the mate that he loved best. So, one and all, they piped up, crying:

"Mother Nature! Let the choosing start! For we'd each fly away with that sweet mate we choose to build a nest in tree or hedgerow and raise our young together!"

UP ONE PAIR OF STAIRS

Now Mother Nature was holding on her hand a lovely, shy young eagle. The eagle had white feathers like a bonnet on her head and all around her neck were more white feathers all afluff and very soft. So sweet was she, so sweet and gentle, that Mother Nature bent and kissed her. Then looking up, good Mother Nature saw before her a fine big eagle, as proud, as grand and powerful as a king. And turning to the other birds, she said:

"This eagle here before me is the greatest of the birds. So he shall have first choice. Until he chooses for himself a mate no other bird shall choose!"

Then that mighty eagle spoke up quickly, saying:

"With all my heart, good Mother, I choose that lovely eagle-maid which you are holding on your hand."

At that the pretty eagle hung her head. She did not answer yes or no, so modest, shy and sweet was she.

But now another mighty eagle cried out fiercely:

"You shall not have that maid! I love her more than you do! She must be mine! Mine! Mine!"

"Nay, nay!" a third great eagle screamed. "I'll have her! That I will! I love her best of all!"

And with that those three great eagles all began to screech. Each cried, "I'll have her!" And while they screeched and argued, not another bird could choose his mate. Well, by-and-by the other birds began to chirp and scold and twitter, for they were all impatient. Each one had seen a pretty bird he wanted for his mate and each one wished to fly away with her to build a nest and raise their young. At last the goose, the cuckoo and the duck all spoke at once.

"Keck, keck! Cuckoo! Quack, quack! If these three eagles can't agree, we pray you, Mother Nature, let us

speak to them and try to end their squabble!"

So Mother Nature answered, "Very well! Speak out!"

Then the falcon said to those three screeching eagles:

"You'll never settle this affair by screeching!"

"That's true! We'll fight!" the eagles screamed.

"Nay!" the falcon answered. "Prove which of you is gentlest! Let not the boldest but the gentlest have the maid!"

Yet still the eagles screeched. So the goose spoke up and said, "Let all these eagles give this maiden up! Let each one choose another mate!"

But then the hawk began to rage, "'Tis like a goose you speak! What bird who calls himself a gentleman would give his true love up and choose another mate?"

"Aye!" cooed the dove. "No lover of a maid should ever change! Not even if she says she will not have him for her mate! He should love her still and serve her all his life!"

"My hat!" then quacked the duck. "What sense is there in that? To wait a lifetime for a maid!"

"Aye! Aye!" agreed the goose. "There's more than one fair birdie one might choose as mate!"

"Fie on you, goose!" the falcon cried. "You geese have never known what true love is!"

"Well I say, let these eagles live alone!" the cuckoo snapped. "Just let them take no mates at all!"

"Live all their lives alone!" the blackbird shrieked. "Who'd have thought of that save you, you cuckoo? No self-respecting bird who lives on seeds could ever have thought up so bad a thing as for a bird to live alone! To think of that it took a murderer like you! You, who pounce on little worms, poor little worms and eat them up!"

And so they quarreled till Mother Nature cried:

"Be still! There's one thing I've not done! I have not asked this eagle-maiden which of these three eagles she would have as mate. So speak up, pretty one! You shall decide this matter. Which one do you choose?"

Then the pretty eagle spoke—shyly, very shyly.

"Almighty Queen, I am so young, so very young! I want no mate at all! Pray let me wait before I choose! Next year, if these three eagles will come back, then—maybe! Maybe?"

"So-be-it!" Mother Nature cried. "She shall not choose until St. Valentine's Day comes round next year!"

At that, those three big eagles drooped their wings and sank their heads down on their breasts. They seemed like sails of ships when all the wind is taken from them.

But Mother Nature turned at last to all the other birds and said, "Now you may choose your mates!"

And then what joy there was among those birds! Each flew off to that sweet birdie he loved best. Then how they sang! Such gladness they poured out! They sang to thank St. Valentine. They sang to welcome summer.

"St. Valentine," they sang, "we thank thee for our mates!"

And then they all sang again—

"To good St. Valentine!
"Thus sing small birdies for thy sake!
Now welcome, Summer, with thy sun so soft!
Thou hast this winter weather beaten back,
And driven away the long, long night's long black!
Well have we reason for to gladden oft!"

The Doll Under the Briar Rosebush

JORGEN MOE

*Translated from the Norwegian by
Gudrun Thorne-Thomsen*

THERE was once a little girl, and her name was Beate. She was only five-years old, but a bright and good little girl she was.

On her birthday her father had given her a beautiful straw hat. There were red ribbons around it; I can't tell you how pretty it was. Her mother had given her a pair of yellow shoes and the daintiest white dress. But her old aunt had given her the very best present of all; it was a doll, with a sweet pretty face and dark brown curls. She was a perfect beauty in every respect. There was nothing the matter with her except that the left eyebrow was painted a tiny bit too high up.

"It looks as if she were frowning a little. I wonder if she is not quite pleased?" asked Beate.

"Oh, yes," answered her aunt, "but she doesn't know you yet. It is a habit she has of lifting her eyebrow a little when she looks closely at anyone. She only wants to find out if you are a good little girl."

"Yes, yes, and now she knows, for now that eyebrow is just like the other one," said Beate.

UP ONE PAIR OF STAIRS

Oh, how Beate grew to love that doll almost more than she loved Marie and Louise, and they were her best friends.

One day Beate was walking in the yard with her doll in her arms. The doll had a new name now, and they had become fast friends. She had called her Beate, her own name, and the name of her old aunt who had given her the doll.

It was early in the spring. There was a beautiful green spot, with fine, soft grass in one corner of the yard around the old well. There stood a big willow tree with a low trunk, and it was covered with the little yellow blossoms that children call goslings. They looked like goslings, too, for each little tassel was soft, soft yellow down and they can swim in the water, but walk? No, that they cannot do.

Now Big Beate—she wasn't more than five-years old, but she was ever so much bigger than the other one—and Little Beate, soon agreed that they would pick goslings from the tree and throw them into the well, so that they might have just as good a time as the goslings that were swimming about in the pond. It was really Big Beate who thought of this first, but Little Beate agreed immediately; you can't imagine how good she always was.

Now Big Beate climbed up into the willow and picked many pretty yellow goslings into her white apron; and, when she counted them and had counted to twenty, twice, she said that now they had enough, and Little Beate thought so too.

So she began to climb down, but that was not easy, for she had to hold her apron together with one hand and climb with the other. She thought Little Beate called up to her to throw the goslings down first, but she didn't dare to do that; she was afraid they might fall and hurt themselves.

UP ONE PAIR OF STAIRS

Now both of them ran over to the well, and Big Beate helped her little friend to get her legs firmly fixed between the logs that were around the well, so that they might sit in comfort and watch the little goslings swim about on the water. Then gosling after gosling was dropped down; and, as soon as each one reached the water, it seemed to become alive and it moved about. Oh, what fun! Big Beate clapped her hands to the pretty little downy birds; and, when she helped Little Beate a bit, she too could clap her hands.

But after a while the little goslings would not swim any longer, but lay quite still. That was no fun at all; so Big Beate asked her namesake if she didn't think she might lean a little over the edge of the well and blow on them, for then she thought they might come to life again. Little Beate didn't answer, but she raised her left eyebrow a good deal and

moved her right arm in the air as if she were saying, "Please don't do that, dear Big Beate! Don't you remember Mother has told us how dark it is down there in the well? Think, if you should fall in!"

"Oh, nonsense; just see how easy it is," said Big Beate, for she thought the goslings were stupid when they didn't want to swim about.

She leaned out over the well and blew on the nearest ones. Yes, it helped, the goslings began to swim again. But those that were farthest away didn't move at all.

"What stupid little things!" said Beate, and she leaned far, far out over the edge of the well. Then her little hands slipped on the smooth log and—splash! In she fell, deep down in the water. It was so cold, so icy cold, and it closed over her head and took the straw hat, which she had got on her birthday, off her hair. She hadn't time to hear if Little Beate screamed, but I'm sure she did.

When Beate's head came over the water again she grasped the round log with both her hands, but the hands were too small and the log so wide and slippery, she couldn't hold on. Then she saw her dear friend, Little Beate, standing stiff and staring at her with her right arm stretched out to her. Big Beate hurriedly caught hold of her and Little Beate made herself as stiff as she could, and stiffer still, and stood there between the logs holding her dear friend out of the water.

Now Beate screamed so loudly that her father and mother heard her and came running as fast as they could, and pulled her out. She was dripping wet and so cold that her teeth chattered.

The father ran to the house with her, but she begged him for heaven's sake not to leave Little Beate, for she might fall into the well, "And it's she who has saved me."

Now they put Beate to bed, and Little Beate had to sleep with her. When she had said her prayers, she hugged her little friend and said, "Never, never can I thank you enough, because you saved me from that deep well, dear Little Beate. Of course, I know that our Lord helped you to stand firm between the logs and to make yourself so strong and stiff, but it was you and no one else, who stretched your hand out to me."

LITTLE BLUE APRON

"LITTLE Blue Apron,
    How do you do?
Never a stocking
And never a shoe!"

Little Blue Apron
    She answered me,
"You don't wear stockings
And shoes by the sea."

"Little Blue Apron—
    Never a hat?
How do you manage
To go out like that?"

"Why, what is the use
    Of a hat?" said she,
"You never wear hats
When you're by the sea."

"Why, little Blue Apron, it seems to me
Very delightful to live by the sea;
But what would hatters and shoemakers do
If every one lived by the sea like you?"

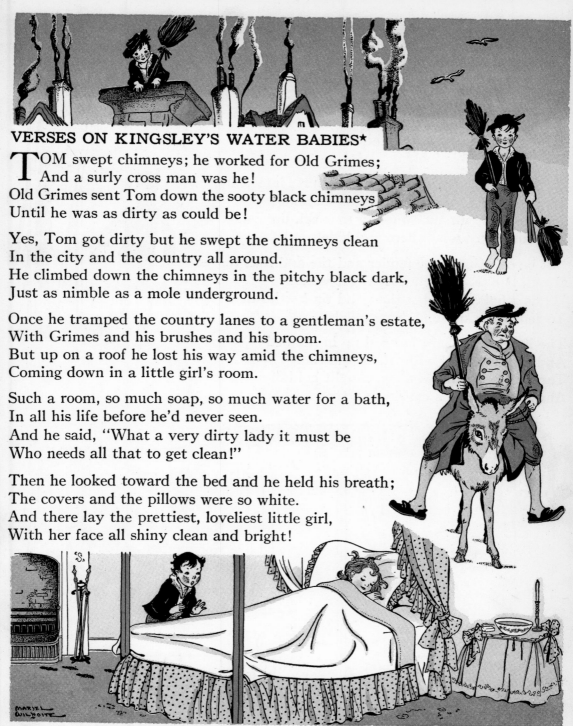

VERSES ON KINGSLEY'S WATER BABIES*

TOM swept chimneys; he worked for Old Grimes;
And a surly cross man was he!
Old Grimes sent Tom down the sooty black chimneys
Until he was as dirty as could be!

Yes, Tom got dirty but he swept the chimneys clean
In the city and the country all around.
He climbed down the chimneys in the pitchy black dark,
Just as nimble as a mole underground.

Once he tramped the country lanes to a gentleman's estate,
With Grimes and his brushes and his broom.
But up on a roof he lost his way amid the chimneys,
Coming down in a little girl's room.

Such a room, so much soap, so much water for a bath,
In all his life before he'd never seen.
And he said, "What a very dirty lady it must be
Who needs all that to get clean!"

Then he looked toward the bed and he held his breath;
The covers and the pillows were so white.
And there lay the prettiest, loveliest little girl,
With her face all shiny clean and bright!

*Born in Devon, Charles Kingsley as a boy lived and played along the seashore with all its adventurous appeal. *Water Babies* and *Westward Ho!* were the natural expression of his great love for the sea and seafaring men.

"Is everyone like that when he's washed?" said Tom.
And he tried to rub the soot off his hand.
Just then he looked around and saw an ugly ape—
Right by his side it seemed to stand!

He turned on the ape—how dared such a thing
Stand close to that pretty little lass?
Then poor Tom saw. He, himself, was the ape,
Reflected in a big looking glass!

He was dirty! He was dirty! He burst into tears,
Tears of shame and of anger and of pride;
And he made for the chimney to sneak up again
And run away somewhere and hide.

But he overthrew the fender and the andirons too—
Crash, bang! What cries! What wails!
'Twas a noise as of ten-thousand tin-kettles tied
To ten-thousand mad dogs' tails!

The little white lady jumped up in her bed
And she screamed with fright, did she.
Tom made for the window, caught hold of a branch
And climbed like a cat down a tree.

Grimes and the gardener saw him dash across the lawn,
And they and the groom gave chase.
Tom made for the woods; they were after him close,
All running at a most terrific pace.

But he gave them the slip and he came out at last
In a meadow by a sparkling little stream;
And he threw himself down on the bank and he said,
"I must, Oh, I *must* be clean!"

He looked in the water so clean and so clear,
With the pebbles at the bottom clean and bright;
But the little silver trout when they saw his dirty face,
All dashed around, splashing in a fright.

He dipped in his hand and the water was so cool;
It was cool.   It was cool, so cool!
He undressed and he said: "I'll be a fish! I'll be clean."
And he jumped in the clearest, cleanest pool.

He swam around a little, then he fell fast asleep,
And he dreamed of the church bells' call,
Of pretty green meadows and cows under trees
And then of nothing at all.

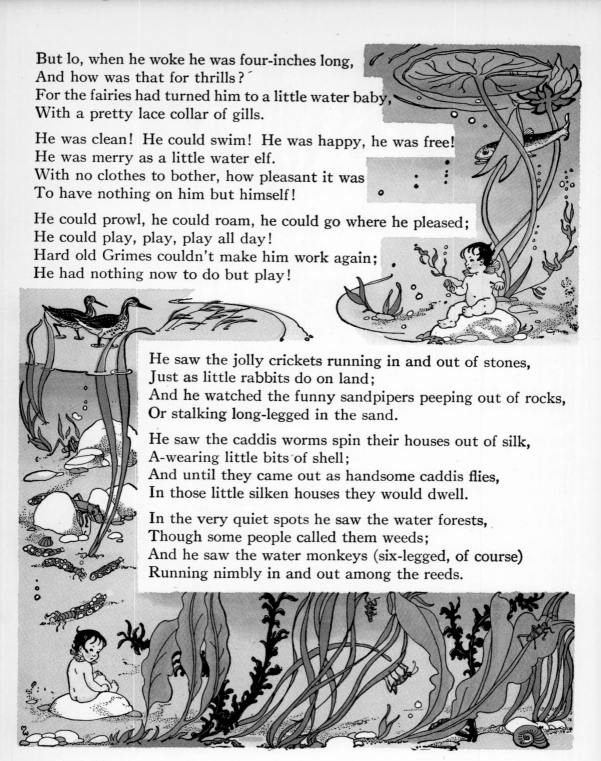

But lo, when he woke he was four-inches long,
And how was that for thrills?
For the fairies had turned him to a little water baby,
With a pretty lace collar of gills.

He was clean! He could swim! He was happy, he was free!
He was merry as a little water elf.
With no clothes to bother, how pleasant it was
To have nothing on him but himself!

He could prowl, he could roam, he could go where he pleased;
He could play, play, play all day!
Hard old Grimes couldn't make him work again;
He had nothing now to do but play!

He saw the jolly crickets running in and out of stones,
Just as little rabbits do on land;
And he watched the funny sandpipers peeping out of rocks,
Or stalking long-legged in the sand.

He saw the caddis worms spin their houses out of silk,
A-wearing little bits of shell;
And until they came out as handsome caddis flies,
In those little silken houses they would dwell.

In the very quiet spots he saw the water forests,
Though some people called them weeds;
And he saw the water monkeys (six-legged, of course)
Running nimbly in and out among the reeds.

There were water flowers, too; he tried to pick them once;
'Twas stars and little bells they seemed to be,
But at his first touch, they turned to jelly balls
And were just as much alive as he.

He played at hare and hounds with the pretty silver trout,
And great fun that was, too;
Before a shower came he would leap from the water,
Just as the little trout do.

How he liked to see the trout rising up at the flies,
As they sailed round and round in the shade,
And the big beetles tumbling in the water with a flop,
In the place where the silver trout played!

And he laughed at caterpillars on their long silken ropes;
For they dropped from the boughs and then
Those foolish little rope dancers changed their foolish minds
And hauled themselves up again!

But one day Tom saw a great big ball
Rolling over, over, over in the stream.
Now it looked like fur, now it shone like glass—
How very strange that ball did seem!

'Then off went Tom to the big dragonfly,
To ask what the ball could be;
But the dragonfly said that he just didn't know;
He was too short-sighted to see.

So Tom swam off and up to the ball.
It was four lovely creatures at play;
They were swimming, rolling, diving,
    twisting, wrestling, cuddling, kissing,
In the very most charming way.

They were otters! They were otters! And the mother
        spied Tom,
Then she said, looking very far from sweet:
"My children, come away! That's an eft, a nasty eft!
He isn't good for you to eat!"

Now an eft is a lizard and Tom felt hurt.
"I'm not an eft," said he.
"For efts have tails!" He turned himself around.
"And I've no tail on me!"

But look! You have hands! You're an eft! You're an eft!
You're no food for gentlefolk to eat.
You may stay where you are till the salmon come along!
Maybe they'll think you'd be a treat!"

"Salmon, what are salmon?" Tom timidly asked;
"The fish we eat!" cried she.
"And they'll be coming soon! For I smell rain!
The rain's coming up off the sea!"

Then the otter proudly dived with a head over heels,
And she grinned like a Cheshire cat.
"But where do the salmon live?" asked Tom,
"I pray you, answer me that!"

"They come from the sea, eft, the wide, wide sea;
They'd be safe there, if they'd stay;
But the silly things come to the river down below
Where we watch for them night and day.

"And when they start down to the sea again,
We follow them evermore;
We toss and we roll in the breakers there
And we have a jolly time on the shore.

"O that's a merry life! It's a merry, merry life,
So my children, come along with me.
We must hurry, hurry, hurry! We must all be on our way,
Down, down, down to the sea!"

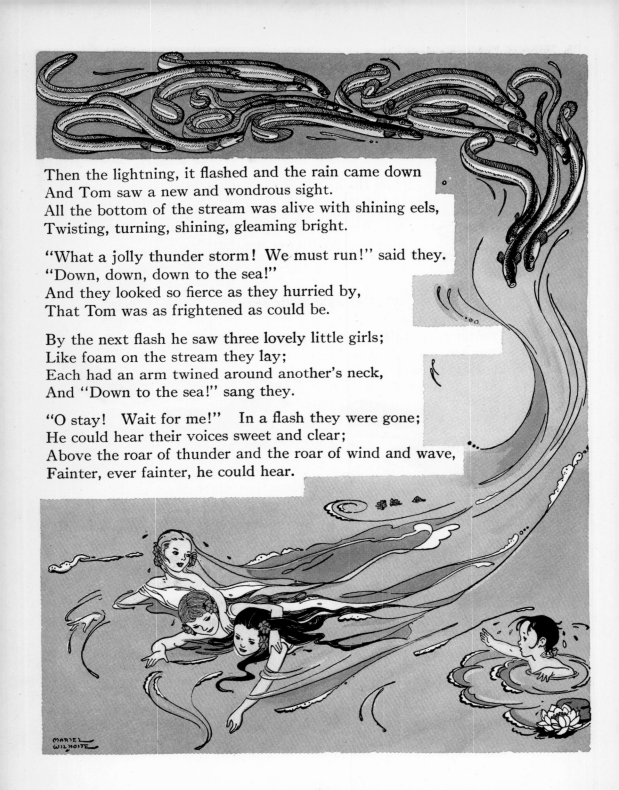

Then the lightning, it flashed and the rain came down
And Tom saw a new and wondrous sight.
All the bottom of the stream was alive with shining eels,
Twisting, turning, shining, gleaming bright.

"What a jolly thunder storm! We must run!" said they.
"Down, down, down to the sea!"
And they looked so fierce as they hurried by,
That Tom was as frightened as could be.

By the next flash he saw three lovely little girls;
Like foam on the stream they lay;
Each had an arm twined around another's neck,
And "Down to the sea!" sang they.

"O stay! Wait for me!" In a flash they were gone;
He could hear their voices sweet and clear;
Above the roar of thunder and the roar of wind and wave,
Fainter, ever fainter, he could hear.

"Everything's going to the sea, O trout,
"I'm off," said Tom, "good-bye!"
But the trout were so busy gobbling up worms
That they didn't even bother to reply!

So Tom started off in the flash of the storm,
And he saw for a moment bright
The tall, tall rocks standing out as clear as day,
But they vanished next instant in the night.

Through the rushing, rushing waters and the roaring cataracts,
Past spots where the water lilies lay,
Through shadows, under bridges, past quiet sleeping towns,
Away went Tom and away.

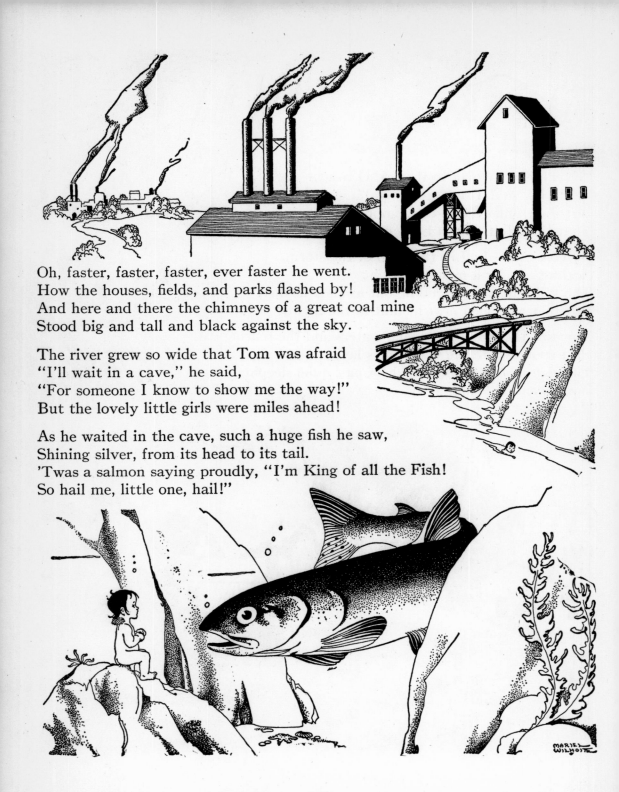

Oh, faster, faster, faster, ever faster he went.
How the houses, fields, and parks flashed by!
And here and there the chimneys of a great coal mine
Stood big and tall and black against the sky.

The river grew so wide that Tom was afraid
"I'll wait in a cave," he said,
"For someone I know to show me the way!"
But the lovely little girls were miles ahead!

As he waited in the cave, such a huge fish he saw,
Shining silver, from its head to its tail.
'Twas a salmon saying proudly, "I'm King of all the Fish!
So hail me, little one, hail!"

With a swish the salmon passed and he made the stream boil,
Then others came, one by one;
Now they leapt from the water high over a rock,
Shining gloriously a moment in the sun.

But in a little time the tide came up,
Bringing salt water in from the sea;
And then what a change came over **Tom**,
He felt so strong and fresh and light and free.

Oh, he leapt in the air and into the stream;
Head over heels, went the boy,
Like salmon when they first feel **the salt** sea brine,
And leap along crazy with **joy**.

The tide was against him, but what did he care?
He could see a dancing buoy far at sea.
"There'll be playmates over there, over there!" he said.
"They'll sport and play all day with me!"

So he swam to the buoy and the little waves danced,
And the sea breeze freshly blew;
And the old buoy danced and the shadows of the clouds
Raced over the bay and flew.

But he found no playmates on that buoy,
And he thought of those girls so sweet.
Then he longed and he longed in his loneliness now
Some other water babies for to meet.

"Do you know, do you know where the water babies live?
To all who passed by he would call.
But some said no and some said yes,
And some said nothing at all.

A fleet of purple snails came a-floating, floating by,
Each on a sponge of foam;
But they said, "We can't tell you, for we float all our lives,
And the middle of the ocean is our home!"

He asked the old sunfish, so flat and so queer,
And the porpoises leaping at play;
But the porpoises answered, "Hush, hush, hush!"
For that was all they'd ever learned to say!

At last he found a lobster who stayed and played with him,
And a very fine lobster was he;
And they played until Tom learned that water babies lived
On St. Brandan's fairy island in the sea!

The island stood on pillars and its roots were full of caves
Where the water babies played all day.
When Tom got there he was happy as could be
And his heart was very merry, light, and gay.

But in time he got uppish. He stole lollypops
And he teased with a naughty, naughty grin;
Till his naughty, naughty naughtiness all came out
In prickles all over his skin.

Then the fairies said, "Tom, you'll have to be taught!
"You're in need of a teacher!" they vowed.
And they brought a little girl, whose beautiful curls
Floated out like a golden cloud.

And the little girl taught Tom how to be good
Till the prickles all vanished away.
Then the little girl said, "Dear me, you're the boy,
Who got into my room that day!"

For the fairies had given little Ellie two wings,
It was she standing there with a smile.
She had flown out the window, over land, over sea,
And off to the water babies' isle.

So Ellie taught Tom for seven years more,
Together they would work and play and roam.
But every single week when Sunday came around,
Little Ellie went off home.

Tom never knew where it was Ellie went
And he grieved when she went away;
For Tom loved Ellie very, very, very much,
And he missed her at work and at play.

Then one day she went and she didn't come back,
Said the fairies, "She'll come no more!
You must go into the world and grow to be a man,
You'll see her then and not before!"

So Tom went out and he learned to be a man,
Then he came once more to the isle.
And there, to be with him forever and a day,
Was Ellie waiting for him with a smile.

MARIEL
WILHOITE